NIGHT SKY
PHOTOGRAPHY

NIGHT SKY
PHOTOGRAPHY

The Moon · the Sun · the Stars · the Planets
Comets · Meteors · Nebulae · Aurorae

H. J. Arnold
Foreword by Patrick Moore

GEORGE
PHILIP

Published by George Philip & Son Ltd
27A Floral Street, London WC2E 9DP

British Library Cataloguing in Publication Data

Arnold, J. J. P.
    Night sky photography: the moon, the sun, the stars,
    the planets, comets, meteors, nebulae, aurorae.
    1. Astronomical photography
    I. Title
    778.9′9523   QB121
    ISBN 0-540-01180-0

Filmset and printed in England by BAS Printers Ltd,
Over Wallop, Hampshire

(*Half title page*) A ten-minute exposure is more
than adequate to demonstrate clearly the apparent
paths of stars at the celestial equator. The region
shown here is between Leo and Virgo and the
equator is about two-thirds of the way up the
frame. If one concentrates on the extreme top and
bottom of the image it is clear that the star trails
arch in opposite directions – i.e. towards the
respective celestial poles. A 50mm f/1.4 lens was
used for this picture and the original was on
Agfachrome 1000RS Professional film.

(*Title page*) This photograph was originally taken
for the cover of a brochure advertising fire-control
equipment for aircraft. This is difficult to illustrate
because fire (particularly in aircraft) is an emotive
subject, and the aim was to suggest the message
without a literal and inevitably staged treatment.
The problem was solved by using one of a
sequence of colour pictures taken at dawn when
aircraft vapour trails were deliberately included in
the composition to frame the rising Sun which
could just be seen through cirrus cloud. In this way
the connection was made between aircraft and fire,
in an image which is still powerful in black and
white.

Contents

For Kit—the sweetest sister there ever was—who did not live to see this book.

Acknowledgements

An author always owes much to those who help so willingly. I appreciated the prompt response from Messrs G.H. Spalding, L.M. Dougherty, D.R.B. Saw and R.J. Livesey – Section Directors of the British Astronomical Association – to my request for assistance. Peter Hingley, the Librarian at the Royal Astronomical Society, dealt with my queries with his usual promptness and efficiency, while Russell Eberst, of the Royal Observatory in Edinburgh, provided considerable guidance on artificial satellites. In this latter context, I am grateful for information on aircraft lights supplied by Captain Frederick Rivett and Senior First Officer Donald Gray of British Airtours. On the somewhat controversial subject of photographing the Sun I benefited from wise counsel willingly provided by Professor John Marshall and Peter Fenton FRCS. I am also indebted to Mr and Mrs R.G.M. Tassell for their kindness in allowing me to take astrophotographs from a site in West Sussex which suffers from less light pollution than my home area.

As to photography, my long-standing and very knowledgeable friends Malcolm Wells, Phillip Lawrence of Kodak Limited and John Pitchforth of Nikon UK Limited, did all that they could to help, and I am greatly indebted to Peter Colligan for all manner of practical assistance upon which it would take at least a full chapter to elaborate. Geoffrey Crawley, Editor of the *British Journal of Photography* and a distinguished photographic scientist, was kind enough not only to give me hours of his time directly but to undertake to read through the draft of the book. Needless to say, it benefited from this attention as it did from that of George T. Keene, a former colleague at the Eastman Kodak Company, who in a private capacity not only read through the manuscript but was good enough to supply one of his own splendid solar images. That kindness was shown also by Akira Fujii, a leading world astrophotographer, who readily despatched images in response to my requests. Dr Stewart Bell was most helpful on optical matters.

In thanking all the above friends and colleagues, I need to state the time-honoured reservation that while they have contributed greatly to whatever quality the book may have, I alone am responsible for any sins of error and omission.

It was my good friend Patrick Moore who suggested to George Philip that my ideas for a book were worth pursuing, and who also graciously accepted the suggestion that he contribute a foreword – though I think both were by way of expiation for helping the car I was driving to sink lower and lower in the sands of the Australian outback when chasing Halley's Comet in 1986! It is said that time passes quickly when you are having fun yet I still cannot believe that it is now more than twenty years since I first appeared with Patrick in *The Sky at Night* to talk about the Lunar Orbiter spacecraft and the film cameras that they carried.

There is always an element of creative tension in working on a book and I have to confess that my normal background level of irascibility tends to increase during such times. Therefore I conclude this acknow-ledgements note by thanking the three generations of ladies in the Arnold household – Ann Helen, Audrey and Dolly – for their forbearance and for providing a steady supply of coffee and soothing words at the appropriate times.

H J P Arnold
Havant, 1987

Picture Acknowledgements

With the exception of the illustrations on pages 77, 116 and 126, by Akira Fujii, and page 85 (bottom), by George T. Keene all photographs are by the author. Unless indicated otherwise, the cameras used to obtain the images were a Nikon F3 or a Nikon F2AS.

The diagrams on pages 101 and 102 are by courtesy of George Y. Haig.

In a number of the images a sequence of three numerals appears in the lower right corner. This is the day, hour and minute the exposure was made printed out by an MF14 data back.

Foreword

Astronomy has become one of the most popular of all hobbies. It is also just about the only science in which amateurs can (and do) make valuable contributions. But looking at the sky, even with binoculars or a telescope, is one thing; taking pictures is quite another – and, according to most books, little can be done except with elaborate equipment quite beyond the financial reach of the average newcomer.

This is why H. J. P. Arnold's book is so valuable, and why it is unlike any other, at least so far as I know. The author is one of the country's leading photographic experts (as his career with Kodak shows), and is also a well-known amateur astronomer. Here, he explains how to make a start in celestial photography, not with highly sophisticated astronomical equipment but with a camera of the type available to many people. How do you take star trails? What can you achieve when two planets come together in conjunc-

tion, presenting a beautiful spectacle which will not recur for years? What if you have the chance to go to see a total eclipse of the Sun – what films do you take, and what exposures do you use? How do you photograph the constellation patterns, bringing out features such as the star clusters and nebulae? You will find the answers here.

The author makes it clear that he is a photographer first and foremost, and takes care to make photographic terms familiar to the astronomical enthusiast who has probably not encountered them before. Therefore, even if you start with a complete ignorance of photography, you will find that by the time you have studied the book you will be quite capable of taking astronomical pictures which will be a constant source of enjoyment to you and to others.

This is a book which fills an important gap in the literature. Read it, and you will see what I mean.

Patrick Moore
Selsey, 1987.

Introduction

The pages of astronomy magazines are full of frequently beautiful and awe-inspiring pictures, many of which are the work not of professional astronomers but of amateurs. With rare exceptions, the pictures owe nothing to luck and everything to application and hard work exercised over the course of years. But all of us have to start some time – and this book is intended to help the newcomer to astrophotography along the first part of the way that may eventually lead to the pages of the astronomy magazines. Even if it does not, there is an enormous amount of satisfaction and enjoyment to be derived from one of the most fascinating hobbies there is (although, to be frank, exasperation and disappointment also are not exactly unknown).

Telescopes are scarcely mentioned in this book. Although they are the primary tool of the astronomer, they require knowledge and skill to be operated competently and it is my view that there is a valuable apprenticeship to be served by the budding astrophotographer in using basic photographic equipment before attempting to use a telescope. However, do not think that the apprenticeship will be dull: a glance at the chapter headings and photographs will show that many types of astrophotography can be attempted with basic equipment – defined as a fixed camera using interchangeable lenses – and need not depend upon equipment of an essentially astronomical nature. Binoculars (7 × 50 models are regarded as a standard) *are* a valuable investment, for they enhance one's vision, have a wide field of view, and can be used for many other purposes.

This book is aimed at two potential readerships. One consists of amateur astronomers, or at least those who know something about astronomy already, who are contemplating a move into astrophotography. The other includes amateur photographers who possibly know little or nothing about astronomy but who admire astronomical images and wonder what is involved. Writing for two readerships inevitably means that a few parts of the book will contain little that is new for some: for example, Chapter 1 (The Sky Above) can be skipped by the astronomers, and the photographers may wish to pass over parts of Chapters 3 and 4 – although Chapter 2 (Another World) constitutes a salutary reminder that the form of photography that lies ahead is decidedly different in some ways from ordinary photography. Whereas astronomers may not feel in need of much extra guidance on photography, photographers should seriously consider reading through one or two of the astronomy books suggested in Sources and Information. In due course they will need also to consider the purchase of a planisphere or star maps, which the astronomers probably have already.

In astrophotography there is no 'golden road' that can be charted. Our individual situations and capabilities and the equipment that we possess all vary so much that it is impossible to present a universal formula. What I can do, however, is sketch a general framework of advice based on some years of practical experience of astrophography. This advice may be regarded as something to consider and can be shaped to suit your preferences and situation. At the very least, it should help to prevent the sort of mistakes that I have made along the way.

In essence the book aims to take its readers to the stage where they can make an important decision: to say in effect that it was fun but they have no wish to take it further – or to make the jump into the world of telescopes, off-axis guiding, hypersensitization and other features beloved of the experienced astrophotographer. Whatever that decision, the book will have succeeded if the choice is made against a background of solid fact, sound knowledge and – hopefully – some achievement.

CHAPTER ONE

The Sky Above

This chapter is intended to outline some of the salient features of the sky and the celestial objects in it that can be recorded on film. It is aimed principally at those with more knowledge of photography than astronomy and the emphasis is on practical rather than theoretical considerations. By the end, I hope that the newcomer to astronomy will broadly understand what is happening in the sky; to complement this understanding it is recommended that you read some of the books mentioned on page 148.

How Big and How Bright?

If a coin is held just in front of one of our eyes it appears very large and blanks out a large area of the field of view. If the same coin is held at arm's length, it appears much smaller – and, if it is placed 100m (329ft) away, it might just be seen as a dot by those with excellent vision. But the size of the coin has not altered in fact in any way. We face this problem when describing the size of celestial objects which can be very close in astronomical terms (a few hundreds of thousands of kilometres) – or so distant that special units of measurement, such as the light year (9.46 million million km/6 million million miles) or the parsec (30.8 million million km/19 million million miles) have been introduced for ease of reference. As luck would have it, there is an excellent example of the effect in our solar system. As seen from Earth, the Sun and the Moon are about the same size but the Moon's diameter is a mere 3476km (2158 miles) compared with the Sun's almost 1.4 million km (860,000 miles).

It is obvious, therefore, that in describing the size of objects in the sky, and in relating their positions one to another, linear measurements cannot be used and we have to turn to the concept of the celestial sphere for help. From ancient times it was imagined that the stars and planets were set in a sphere with the Earth at the centre. This is not true, but the sphere does present a method of sizing any object as seen from Earth. We can imagine a full or great circle running around the equator of the sphere for 360 degrees and another passing through the celestial poles and directly overhead (the zenith). The angle from horizon to horizon will be 180 degrees and from the horizon to a point directly overhead, 90 degrees. This therefore provides an angular system of measurement with the vertex of the measured angle located at the observer's eye. (The vertex is a geometrical term for the point at which an angle diverges.)

There are some helpful, rough and ready methods of estimating angular distances that the newcomer can adopt. When the arm is fully extended, a clenched fist covers an area of sky about 10 degrees across (nine fists to zenith!) and the little finger about one degree across. Since the angular size of the full Moon is around half a degree the area covered by the little finger can be tested by establishing that the lunar disc is easily hidden or occluded by the little finger positioned at arm's length. Of course, the system is capable of much more accuracy than this suggests.

One degree is composed of sixty minutes (usually referred to as arc minutes to distinguish them from units of time), for which the symbol is ′, and each minute of sixty arc seconds, for which the symbol is ″. Thus the angular sizes of both the Sun and Moon are about thirty minutes. The planets and stars are small enough when seen from Earth to be measured in terms of arc seconds.

In discussing the size of objects I have avoided the term magnitude quite deliberately because, rather perversely, astronomers use it to describe the brightness of celestial objects. The scale used is still basically that devised by the Greek astronomer and mathematician Hipparchus in the second century BC. He described the brightest stars that could be seen with the naked eye (Hipparchus lived almost two millennia before the invention of the telescope) as being of the first magnitude and the faintest as of the sixth magnitude. Each successive magnitude change involves a brightness difference of 2.5 times − which means that a first magnitude star is one hundred times (or five magnitudes) brighter than a sixth magnitude star. Hence, the brighter the star the lower the magnitude.

Not surprisingly, the system has been considerably refined since the time of Hipparchus. Magnitudes have been measured to decimal values (using instruments called photometers) and the brightest objects accorded negative values − such as Sirius (the brightest star in the sky), Arcturus in Bootes, and Canopus in the southern constellation Carina. Sirius is surpassed in brightness by Jupiter and Mars some of the time − depending on their positions relative to the Sun and Earth − and Venus, the full Moon and the Sun all of the time. Sirius has a magnitude of −1.4, Venus at its brightest −4.4, the full Moon −12.7 and the Sun −26.8.

As with size, a note of caution has to be sounded on the matter of brightness. Stars differ enormously in luminosity and distance from Earth, so the magnitudes indicated above are what are referred to as apparent or visual magnitudes. Values have been calculated for the magnitudes stars would have if they were to be viewed from a standard distance of ten parsecs, and these are known as absolute magnitudes. The calculation for Sirius and Polaris is enlightening. To our eyes Polaris is a very ordinary star and has an apparent magnitude of 2 compared with the −1.4 of Sirius. However, the absolute magnitude of Sirius is only +1.3 and that for Polaris −4.6, which is brighter than Venus. Hence Polaris is in fact far more luminous than Sirius but its far greater distance from Earth makes it appear much dimmer. More chastening still is the calculation for our star, the Sun. Viewed from ten parsecs it would be magnitude +4.8 – a dim object, albeit visible with the naked eye.

None the less, it is apparent magnitudes which are of the greatest concern to the budding astrophotographer. Cameras and films enable us to record stars far dimmer than those discernible to the human eye and since our galaxy is estimated to contain about 100,000 million stars it is extremely interesting to calculate some of the numbers. There are 20 first magnitude stars, 65 second magnitude, 190 third magnitude, 425 fourth magnitude, 1100 fifth magnitude and 3200 sixth magnitude. That makes a total of 5000 naked-eye stars, which means – allowing for the fact that we only see approximately one half of the celestial sphere during our night – that about 2500 stars only are visible to us without the aid of binoculars or telescopes. From magnitude 6, the numbers grow rapidly – 13,000 seventh magnitude, 40,000 eighth magnitude, 142,000 ninth magnitude and, moving on, it is calculated that there are possibly five million stars between magnitudes 11 and 12. Although we cannot see them individually with the naked eye, in total they

contribute to the general luminosity of the night sky and nowhere more so than in the Milky Way, a band in the sky created by a line-of-sight effect as we look inwards towards the centre of our galaxy from our position on the edge of one of the spiral arms.

The Way We See

Before setting out to study the movement (real or apparent) of the stars and planets, and the part that Earth itself plays, it will be helpful to describe briefly an important attribute of the human eye. The retina is the light-sensitive membrane at the back of the eye which receives the image formed by the lens. This quality is conferred by millions of two different types of sensitive elements – rods and cones, which are named after their characteristic shapes. The cones distinguish colour and operate best in bright light conditions. The rods cannot discriminate colour and are most sensitive in low light conditions. Time is needed for the rods to accommodate to dark conditions and this is referred to as dark adaptation.

The cones are concentrated in the central area of the retina and are the only elements in the *fovea centralis*, a small area of the retina where the eye possesses its highest resolving power. Away from the fovea the rods rapidly begin to predominate and form an oval ring around it. This explains one of the most important facts about looking at the night sky, and in particular searching for dim objects. If the eye is concentrated directly on the area of interest the object may not be resolved because of the cones' poor performance in low light conditions. However, if it looks off-axis slightly, towards one side of the object's suspected position, the superior low light performance of the rods gathered around the fovea is far more likely to result in the eye discriminating the object. This observing technique is known as averted vision and is one of the most valuable techniques we can learn as we set out on the journey around the skies.

The Map of the Sky

Imagine for a few moments that we are on a planet just like Earth but that there is no Sun, so night is unbroken for each rotation of the planet. Just like Earth, it revolves from west to east (anticlockwise as seen from a vantage point over the north pole, clockwise from over the south pole). As the hours pass, a panorama of stars travels across the sky from east to west until the time comes for the pattern to start being repeated. Relative to each other as seen from Earth the positions of the stars change very little over the centuries so it is not too difficult to project the positions of the stars in this imaginary celestial sphere on to flat, two-dimensional maps as we do with Earth.

The Earth's equator can be projected to form the celestial equator, and the geographical poles the celestial poles in the sky. A co-ordinate system like latitude and longitude is needed – and in star maps latitude becomes declination, which is expressed in degrees in '+' or '−' terms to indicate a position north or south of the celestial equator up to a maximum of ninety degrees at the celestial poles. The east–west co-ordinate system is termed right ascension and is expressed in terms of hours, minutes and seconds with a maximum of twenty-four hours representing the Earth's rotation period. (Since one complete revolution equals 360 degrees, one hour of right ascension represents 360/24 = 15 degrees.) As with the use of the Greenwich meridian in the longitude system, in mapping the stars the point or line selected for the start of the twenty-four hour clock is entirely arbitrary. It concerns the Sun but since, for the moment, we are not dealing with the Sun, the explanation will follow later.

Over the course of a full rotation of our dayless planet, an observer at the north (or south) pole will see the respective pole star areas at zenith and the celestial equator will be on the horizon. The same half of the sky will always be seen (northern or southern hemisphere only) and all the stars will revolve around the celestial pole with none rising or setting – i.e. they will all be circumpolar. At the equator, an observer will see the entire celestial sphere from the south to north celestial poles rotate across the sky in the twenty-four hours. Every star will rise and set and each will do so at a right angle to the eastern or western horizon. Between the two extreme locations, some stars will be circumpolar (as Ursa Major is from the UK, for example) but others will set, their slant angle to the horizon when rising or setting being 90 degrees less the latitude; e.g. at a latitude of 51°N the slant angle will be 39 degrees towards the south. (The slant angle for rising and setting constellations seen from the southern hemisphere is to the north.)

For a northern hemisphere observer at 51°N, any star with a declination of +51 will be directly overhead when the star is on the meridian, the imaginary line through the north and south celestial poles. From such a location, it follows that the farther south the declination of a constellation, the lower its position in the sky. From that latitude, for

The Ecliptic

The ecliptic is the name given to the path which the Sun appears to follow against the background of the stars during the course of a year, although it is, in fact, the movement of the Earth about the Sun which creates this effect. Because of the tilt of the Earth's axis at an angle of 23.5°, the ecliptic traces the somewhat complex path seen above. The dotted line represents the apparent movement of the Sun, and the lines on either side the boundaries beyond which the planets, all of which have a slightly different inclination to the ecliptic, do not stray as seen from Earth. The diagram demonstrates why constellations are seen at certain times of the year; for example, in January Sagittarius is close to the Sun (RA19), whereas twelve RA hours away constellations such as Taurus and Gemini are high in the night sky at midnight when seen from northern latitudes.

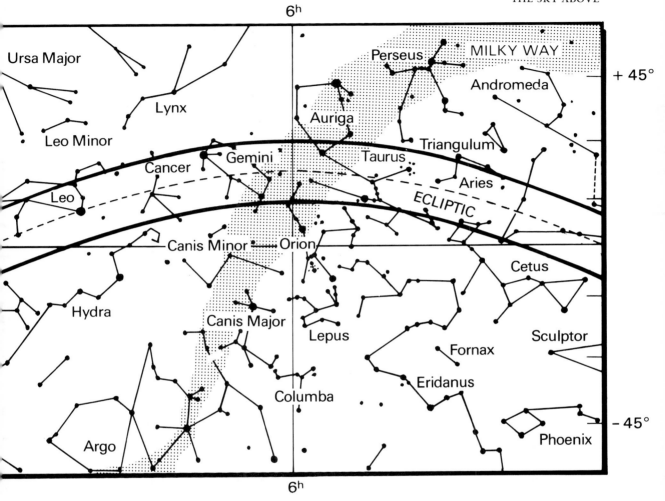

example, Leo is never as high as Ursa Major, and Orion (which straddles the celestial equator) never as high as Leo. Capricornus, at around −15 degrees declination, is lower still and we eventually reach the stage where constellations are so far south in declination that they never rise for northern observers at higher latitudes. Thus, the Southern Cross can never be seen from the UK or most of the USA. The reverse is true, of course, for southern observers viewing northern declination constellations. It is appropriate to point out here that the constellations are line-of-sight effects as viewed from Earth and are not groupings that are genuinely associated.

The Sun

Now, having explained in outline about the apparent movement of the stars and their positions in the sky − neither of which changes, in essence, from century to century − let us look at the Sun. Here there are two effects to consider: what happens as the Earth orbits the Sun in a period of a little more than 365 days, and what happens as a result of the Earth's daily rotation on its axis. (For the time being we will ignore the other planets.)

As the Earth orbits the Sun during the year the latter appears to pursue a path against a background of stars, and this is called the ecliptic. The ecliptic does not, unfortunately, run neatly along the celestial equator, because the Earth's axis is tilted at an angle of 23.5 degrees to the perpendicular to the plane in which it orbits the Sun. This causes the Sun's apparent path to appear as in the diagram. It reaches its farthest point north (declination +23.5 degrees) on about 22 June when it is overhead in the Tropic of Cancer at latitude 23.5°N − and its farthest point south around

22 December when it is similarly located over the Tropic of Capricorn at latitude 23.5°S. The Sun appears to remain at about the same altitude for a few days, hence the name given to these events − solstices, meaning 'standing still of the Sun'. The June date represents midsummer in the northern hemisphere and midwinter in the southern; the December date represents midsummer in the southern hemisphere and midwinter in the northern.

The dates on which the Sun crosses the celestial equator on its apparent annual journey (22 March and 22 September) are called the vernal and autumnal equinoxes respectively. The arbitrary starting point from which right ascension (RA) is measured (referred to earlier), is at the spring equinox when the Sun is in the constellation Pisces, which can be verified in the diagram on pages 16 and 17.

At the beginning of the chapter, we imagined the movement of the stars across the sky for twenty-four hours without the Sun. Now that we have included the Sun, the diagram enables us to see without the need to consult any other document (or even to check the sky) which constellations will be visible at night and which will be lost in the glare of the Sun at any time of the year. Thus on 5 January, the Sun is in Sagittarius (RA19), so that constellation cannot be seen, but those constellations differing by twelve RA hours (i.e. at RA7) will be seen well in the winter skies at midnight − for example, Auriga, Gemini, Taurus and Orion. Incidentally, a practical record of the Sun's apparent movement in the sky during the course of an entire year (which forms a figure of eight and is called an analemma) has been photographed at least once in recent years, which must be a record for dedicated time-lapse photography. The two loops of the figure '8' are not equal in size, which results from the Earth's orbit about the Sun being elliptical.

Now we can consider the matter of the Earth's rotation. Relative to the stars, the Earth completes its daily revolution in a little over twenty-three hours fifty-six minutes. That is known as the sidereal day. But the Earth moves about one degree a day in its orbit around the Sun although, of course, as seen from Earth it is the Sun that appears to move by that amount. Therefore, by the end of any one day, the Earth has to rotate not 360 degrees but 361 degrees to complete a solar day. The extra degree represents four minutes in time which makes a solar day of exactly twenty-four hours.

The difference between the solar and sidereal days means that the stars rise four minutes earlier every day. Thus stars that are just rising at 22.00 on 1 September will be rising at 20.00 on 1 October (30 × 4 minutes = 2 hours) and, moreover, this will occur year in and year out. This four-minute daily 'gain' by the stars is one way of explaining why they eventually move into daytime (and then back again into night). Also, it is a relatively simple task to project the rising or setting times backwards or forwards when we have information for one month. Thus in the example above, the stars rising at 22.00 on 1 September were rising at midnight on 1 August and 02.00 on 1 July. Moving the other way, they will be rising at 18.00 on 1 November and, say, 14.00 on 1 January. By the way, astronomers usually express all twenty-four hour clock times in terms of Universal Time (UT) which, fortunately for those of us in the UK, equates with GMT.

Many individual stars in the constellations have Arabic names but they are also identified by Greek letters, a system introduced by the seventeenth-century German astronomer Johann Bayer. Nebulae, star clusters and the occasional galaxy are listed by Messier numbers (e.g. M31 – the Great Galaxy in Andromeda) after the French astronomer who classified them, but to add a little confusion, a New General Catalogue of Clusters and Nebulae, published in the late nineteenth century, proposed NGC numbers that were intended to supersede the Messier numbers, and although the latter still remain in use, NGC numbers exist as well.

One point about the RA/declination (or RA/Dec) system, which may confuse newcomers at least briefly, is that a location identified by latitude and longitude co-ordinates on Earth does not move (unless viewed by an observer in space). But the effects of the Earth's rotation cause any location on the celestial sphere to appear to move. Thus Spica in the constellation Virgo (RA13.23 Dec −11.00 degrees) obviously rises, passes through meridian and sets. A major value of the RA/Dec system is that it establishes the positions of the stars and other deep space objects permanently relative to one another.

The Planets

The diagram overleaf presents some useful information about all nine planets of the solar system in a compact form. Doubt is now being expressed as to whether Pluto is a genuine planet – it seems much out of place in the realm of the gas giants Jupiter, Saturn, Uranus and Neptune – but that need not bother us here since we are primarily concerned with setting the scene.

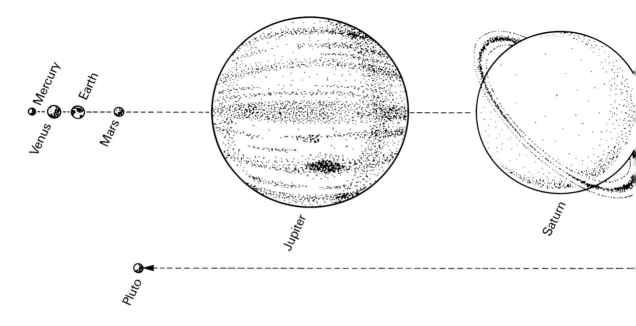

The Planets of the Solar System

In the diagram above, the major planets of the Solar System are drawn to scale, both in relative sizes and distance from one another. The great difference in size between the two gas giants (Jupiter and Saturn) and the inner planets (Mercury, Venus, Earth and Mars), as well as tiny Pluto, is easily seen. The table gives detailed information about the individual planets, and underlines the great variety to be found; for example, Pluto's 'year' is equal to almost 250 Earth years.

The planets orbit the Sun in broadly the same plane but all have slightly different inclinations. Ignoring Pluto's inclination of more than 17 degrees, all the others do not stray far from the ecliptic as seen from Earth – the biggest inclination is that of Mercury at seven degrees. This fact gives additional meaning to the diagram on pages 16–17 which shows a belt seven or eight degrees on either side of the ecliptic. This belt is known as the Zodiac and, stretching all around the sky,

	Mercury	Venus	Earth	Mars	Jupiter	Saturn	Uranus	Neptune	Pluto
Mean Distance From Sun (Millions of Kilometres)	57·9	108·2	149·6	227·9	778·3	1,427	2,869	4,496	5,900
Equatorial Diameter (Kilometres)	4,880	12,104	12,756	6,787	142,800	120,400	51,800	49,500	3,500

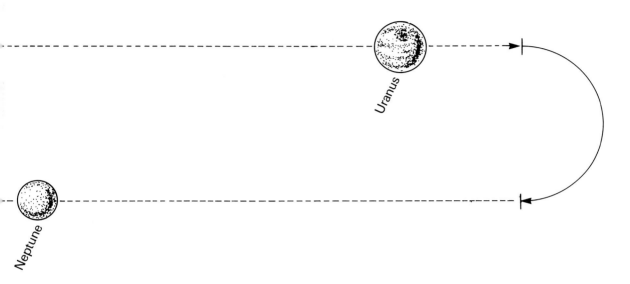

constitutes the region where Sun, Earth, Moon and all the planets – again with the exception of Pluto – are always found. (The belt runs through the twelve zodiacal constellations and through parts of several others which are not granted the honour of that name.) A glance at the diagram, therefore, will show that a planet will never be found in Ursa Major or Hercules in the northern sky, nor will one be found in Centaurus or Grus in the southern sky.

Mercury and Venus, are known as inferior planets because their orbits lie inside that of Earth. This means that they show varying phases as they orbit the Sun, and with angular distances from the Sun of never more than thirty degrees (in the case of Mercury) and

forty-seven degrees (in the case of Venus) they are essentially evening or dawn objects for naked-eye viewing. It follows that they can never be seen all through the night.

Earth and Mars – like Mercury and Venus – are essentially rocky planets, but beyond Mars and the asteroid belt (which may or may not be the site of a planet that failed) lie the gas giants. Once again the diagram presents useful information on relative sizes and distances between each other. The length of time it takes the slower moving outer planets to traverse a given area of the sky is well suggested by the comparison that if Mars travels through a given constellation in two months, Saturn will take about two-and-a-half years, and Neptune more than fourteen years. One useful result of this is that once one of the outer planets is in our night sky it will remain there for quite some months.

All the planets proceed at their varying speeds in an easterly direction, but one line-of-sight effect (which occurs most dramatically in the case of Mars) may puzzle newcomers. Occasionally Mars stops in its easterly movement, appears to move west for a short while and then resumes its motion to the east. This is called a retrograde motion. What happens is that Earth moves faster than Mars (its year is not far off half that of the Red Planet) and sometimes the two bodies are in relative positions on the same side of the Sun whereby Earth can 'catch up' with Mars and pass it. When this happens Mars appears to perform a backward loop until normal apparent motion is restored.

Because the planets are all in orbit about the Sun, it will be evident that – unlike the stars – their positions in the sky cannot be represented on an unchanging map. The normal and quite logical method of showing their positions month by month is to superimpose them on a background chart of the stars.

The Moon

The Moon can dominate the sky on many nights, particularly when it is full or gibbous (between half and full). It shines, like the planets, by reflected light from the Sun and although it appears so bright (because it is in a largely dark sky and there is nothing to rival it) its dark surface reflects only seven per cent of the incident sunlight. In that, it is markedly inferior to Venus, for example, but we see a lot more of it from Earth than we do of Venus.

Compared with other planet/moon systems, the Moon is so large relative to Earth

that the debate about the satellite's origins still continues. Its orbit about Earth is elliptical and it moves eastwards against the celestial background at the rate of about one diameter (3476km/2158 miles) per hour, or thirteen degrees in twenty-four hours. This accounts for the fact that it rises later each night.

The Moon's sidereal month is completed in about 27.3 days and because this is the period it takes to spin once on its axis, we see broadly the same hemisphere all the time from Earth. What is called the synodic month – the time it takes for the Moon to orbit the Earth and become aligned with the Earth, Moon and Sun once more – is approximately 29.5 days. This is the period between new or full Moons. (The far side was not seen until the coming of the space era.)

Most of the pictures of the Moon reproduced later were taken when it was full. However, as the terminator – or boundary between night and day – moves across the lunar surface craters, mountains and other details are clearly revealed by the low sunlight angle on the daylight side of the terminator. A fascinating and instructive exercise is to photograph the Moon at as frequent intervals as possible through a month (*opposite and following pages*), and – using a good lunar chart – to study the features revealed by the progress of a lunar day across the surface. The pictures are of (a) a five-day waxing crescent, (b) a seven-day or half-phase Moon, (c) a thirteen-day waxing gibbous disc, (d) a twenty-day waning gibbous Moon and (e) a twenty-three day waning crescent. As an example, notice how the great crater Tycho in the southern hemisphere of the Moon is seen to best advantage in (d) as the terminator approaches from the east: compare it with the previous image.

B

c

D

E

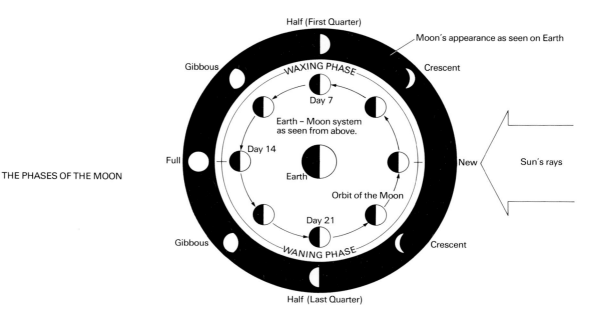

THE PHASES OF THE MOON

The phases of the Moon are demonstrated in the diagram. This shows that a waxing crescent Moon of a few days can be only an early evening object in a dark sky, whereas its waning counterpart can rise only shortly before dawn. Similarly, a full Moon must rise in the east as the Sun sets in the west. Artistic licence – or ignorance – in paintings and composite photographs all too often depict the Moon in a manner which is physically impossible.

Eclipses

One final explanation is needed for those interpreting the diagram of lunar phases. Looking at the diagram, it would be quite logical to assume that solar eclipses occur every time the Moon is new and lunar eclipses every time the Moon is full. In fact, both sorts of eclipses are relatively infrequent because of the tilt of the Moon's orbit – it is inclined at about five degrees to the ecliptic. This means that for much of the time when the Sun, Moon and Earth may appear to be in alignment, the Moon is above or below the ecliptic. It is only when the Moon is at the two points (nodes) of its orbit that intersect the ecliptic at the same time as there is an alignment that a solar or lunar eclipse will occur. Partial eclipses take place if the alignment is not quite perfect. We owe the existence of the beauty of a total solar eclipse to the sheer chance that, as seen from the Earth, the two other bodies are about the same angular size.

CHAPTER TWO

Another World

Many forms of photography are difficult or demanding – and sometimes even dangerous – particularly in professional practice. As far as the amateur is concerned, astrophotography makes demands of a technical kind as well as on personal attitudes. The technical demands, moreover, involve some features which will be new to even experienced 'everyday' photographers. Astrophotography may be described, indeed, as 'another world'.

Before anything can be done, you have to find the subject – a task which does not bother most other photographers. When the subject is the Moon the exercise is usually very easy (except when it is newly risen and totally eclipsed), but other targets can be more difficult. Locating a constellation and checking that the field of view of the chosen lens includes the entire constellation requires some elementary knowledge of astronomy. But as the subjects become fainter and the powers of magnification need to be higher, the search becomes harder; also, the low light levels and consequent lengthy exposures need to be considered more closely. The classic everyday exposure of $\frac{1}{125}$ of a second at f/11 may well be used to photograph a full Moon with a moderate speed film but, as one moves to other subjects such as the stars or meteors, then exposures lengthen considerably. For example, an exposure of 125 seconds – which many everyday photographers may never have used in their lives – would be regarded by astrophotographers as quite short for some subjects. As one progresses to more demanding subjects, exposures of many minutes become the order of the day (or, rather, night).

There is a corollary to this consideration of low light levels. A keen ordinary photographer fully realizes the importance of focusing accurately (some newer cameras accomplish this automatically, of course) and will make this an important, albeit obvious, part of technique. Usually such a procedure is easy – not so for the astrophotographer. This may sound very surprising because you might think that only one focusing distance would be used in astrophotography – that of infinity. However, whereas virtually all shorter focal length lenses have a fixed infinity setting, some top-quality telephoto lenses of modest focal length can be focused beyond the nominal infinity setting to compensate for temperature changes – this is true of most catadioptric, or mirror-reflex, photographic lenses (as well as telescopes). If the target is a dim object then focus becomes an important issue for the astrophotographer and the availability of special, bright viewing screens in the more advanced camera systems helps to make focusing much easier.

When we learn to photograph everyday subjects, a primary concern is to establish the correct exposure for various subjects. With experience, we learn that the matter is not quite as clear cut and that somebody who, for example, likes a black and white print with strong contrasts may well give a different exposure from another photographer, despite using a film of the same speed. The non-existence of what might be called universally correct exposures for different subjects is very much part of the experienced astrophotographer's creed.

Any exposure aimed at achieving optimum quality is the product of a complex combination of factors involving equipment, film, subject, procedures and conditions, and can vary greatly. A straightforward example is that of the Moon photographed at different times as it rises from the horizon. An exposure made as it comes into view over the horizon (and shines through the maximum depth of atmosphere) could easily differ by a full stop from one made when the Moon is at its maximum altitude and shines through the minimum depth of atmosphere. Similarly, some stars (those called, appropriately enough, variables) and the planets (in different parts of their orbit as seen from Earth) vary intrinsically in brightness quite apart from the effects of the atmospheric conditions through which we view them. Calculating exposures will be dealt with at greater length later but it is appropriate here to stress the need to allow for variations, which in terms of practical photography means the need to bracket a number of different exposures around a starting point which itself will be indicated by calculation and/or experience.

This is a major reason why it is so important for the astrophotographer to get into the habit from the beginning of keeping detailed notes – something that the everyday photographer rarely needs to do. It is on the basis of these notes (which should give information about the equipment/film combination used as well as the local viewing conditions and other relevant factors upon which no distant 'expert' can meaningfully advise) that recurring subjects can be tackled with more confidence, new ones approached with greater insight and, in general, experience developed and progress made.

Although it will be dealt with later in more detail, there is one fundamental difference between the photographic theory and practice of astrophotography and that of many other forms of photography. To the ordinary photographer the measure of the speed of a lens is its f-number, or focal ratio. The focal ratio is one vital factor in the calculation of a photographic exposure – the three others being shutter speed, film sensitivity and the brightness of the subject. It is a value derived from dividing the focal length of the lens by its diameter. The focal length of a lens has a direct bearing on the image size of a subject. Assuming the diameter of a lens stays the same, increasing the focal length spreads the image of a subject – formed from the same amount of light – over a greater area of the film and this reduces the intensity of the light; that is, the lens is said to be slower. If we double a focal length the area of the image is four times greater, because it is proportional to the square of the focal length. So, if we double the focal length of a 50mm focal length f/2 lens of 25mm diameter we have a 100mm/25mm = f/4 focal ratio lens. The everyday photographer understands the importance of f-number in exposure calculations but in astronomy a new situation is confronted, though not all the time.

When we photograph the Moon, or a comet, or an aurora, they have a size on the film which relates directly to the focal length of the lens in use – just as in ordinary photography. The Moon, which is quite a reasonably sized disc when recorded on the film frame of a 35mm camera with a 250mm focal length lens, doubles in size when a 500mm focal length lens is used. Celestial objects of this kind behave just like those photographed by the everyday hobbyist, and astronomers and astrophotographers refer to them as extended objects. But stars are so far away that to all intents and purposes focal lengths (no matter how big) continue to render them only as point sources. They are therefore not extended objects and the measure of how fast or slow a lens is in recording them is judged by the size of its diameter and not focal ratio. The same applies to the planets until (since they are not so far away) we reach focal lengths which record them individually as something more than points of light. Then they become extended objects where once again focal ratio becomes a major concern in calculating exposures.

This point has been stressed at this relatively early stage in the book because it could be a source of confusion to quite experienced photographers. If you asked them to choose the faster of two lenses – a 35mm f/1.4 and a 180mm f/2.8 – quite understandably they would choose the former and they would be correct for extended objects. But for photographing the stars they would be wrong, because the former has a lens diameter of 25mm (35/1.4) whereas the latter has a diameter of more than 64mm (180/2.8). Hence, when using the same film, a camera fitted with the 180mm lens would record considerably fainter stars over a given period of time than the 50mm.

There is one other potential source of confusion – between astronomers and photographers this time – which needs to be highlighted. It arises from the manner in which the two groups refer to telescopes and lenses. The terms '35mm', '180mm', '250mm' are used by photographers to refer to lenses. They are an indication of the focal length of the lenses and thereby of the relative size of images produced on the film. Among astronomers, however, these terms refer to the diameter or aperture of a telescope objective or lens – their main concern being the light-gathering capability of their telescopes (just as the references to diameters of lenses above concerned the speed of the lens in capturing stars as point sources). Throughout this book such references will be used in the photographic sense of focal length and the diameter of a lens will be referred to quite specifically as such. Fortunately focal ratio has the same meaning for both astronomers and photographers.

Astrophotography is set apart from other forms of photography by natural and human considerations which have nothing to do with purely photographic matters. So far as nature is concerned, the everyday photographer often seeks ideal circumstances but can usually make do without. But how do you photograph the stars through clouds? Further, although clouds may not be present, the photographic or observing quality of the atmosphere can vary greatly (astronomers usually call it the 'seeing'). It may surprise the newcomer to learn that seemingly beautiful nights with a clear sky full of twinkling stars are often a sign of considerable atmospheric turbulence – and therefore bad seeing – whereas nights that are ostensibly less clear and suggestive of a little high haze can be much better because the haze results from less disturbed conditions in the atmosphere. Only experience and results on film can provide the key. Sometimes even the major subjects in astrophotography can conspire against us: for example, all too often the Moon will be strong when we want to photograph meteors – which are thus rendered almost invisible.

Obviously by definition the astrophotographer will most often operate at night. At any time of night the delights of the British climate can create problems not faced in some other parts of the world. For example, condensation will result once the temperature of the front element of a lens falls below that of the surrounding air. (It is significant that astronomers use the term 'dew cap' for what photographers call a 'lens hood'.) The problem can be dealt with but it indicates the greater challenge to the astrophotographer posed by cold temperatures. There is a serious need to dress warmly and not be dissuaded by any comments from one's family or friends about looking as though one is going on an Arctic expedition.

Man compounds the problems caused by nature. Urban areas of many countries are swamped by light pollution which makes observing difficult if not impossible – and astrophotography often even more so. As citizens we understand the need for much of this lighting but the astronomer may be forgiven for looking quizzically at the bulk of street lights which are designed in such a way that they direct almost as much light upwards (and uselessly) as they do downwards, where it is wanted. In towns we no longer have a dark sky – it is all too often an orange-grey. It may therefore be necessary to travel to get away from the worst effects.

Astrophotography is not for those who cannot resist the comfort of retiring to a warm bed – nor for those unprepared to rise from one during the course of the night. These are the disciplinary demands of the calling: if an event occurs in the skies in the early hours then the staunch astrophotographer must be up and about to record it – unless, for the lucky few, automated equipment is left on patrol. Similarly, in areas where the weather is fickle one must strive to be resolute and photograph an object of interest as soon as the weather allows – to put it off because there is something of interest on TV reveals that we are not made of the 'right stuff'.

As astrophotographers we need to realize our vulnerability to Murphy's Law, which is usually referred to by astronomers as Spode's Law. This states not only that if something can go wrong it will, but that it will go wrong in the worst possible circumstances. Thus a lengthy time exposure will be ruined by the cat knocking the tripod, or your sneezing and hitting it with an arm, not at the beginning of an exposure but just before the end so that the maximum amount of time is wasted. Similarly, if due care is not being taken, it will be at the end of, rather than early in, a session that you will discover that there has been an equipment malfunction. Spode's Law also dictates that upon the arrival of a British party at Alice Springs in Australia rain will start to fall immediately and that Halley's Comet, having displayed a prominent tail for some weeks before, should lose it.

When this slightly tongue-in-cheek account of the astrophotographer's world is read by likely recruits there is a chance that they might be dissuaded from entering it. (It could be even worse, for the saying is that the average success rate in astrophotography is perhaps one in twelve exposures, or twenty-four if the photographer is very good, or lucky!) This would be a great pity. It is true that to do reasonably well and to progress even in the early stages of astrophotography requires an application and a preparedness to be methodical that will not be found among the casually interested nor among those who wish a subject to be 'easy'. But what enjoyment is there in practising that which is easy, what sense of achievement?

For those willing to make an effort, to learn from mistakes and to suffer the inevitable assaults of Spode's Law, with fortitude and a sense of humour, the rewards and enjoyment are great. There is above us a magnificent panorama and to seek to capture parts of it on film is a task of endless challenge which makes the successes all the sweeter. This book is intended to help those wishing to take up the challenge. Read on . . .

CHAPTER THREE

Equipment

The Camera

It is as well to state the bad news first: the 'compact' cameras which have been so successful in recent years are totally unsuitable for astrophotography because they have no 'B' shutter function permitting the manually controlled time exposures that are an essential feature of astrophotography. This sweeping statement is slightly unfair in that it is possible to use one of the compacts loaded with fast film to photograph a pictorial sky scene at twilight featuring perhaps clouds with the Moon and very bright planets – but this is the extent of any capability and cannot be regarded as sufficient.

Given the availability of a 'B' shutter setting, several camera types may be at least adequate for astrophotography. A twin lens reflex, for example, would be suitable for photographing constellations. Parallax would be no problem (with the subject at infinity) and the normal right-angle viewfinder would be a positive advantage – as will be elaborated later. Similarly, a non-reflex rangefinder type could be used at least for star photography. A basic limitation with both types, however, is that most makes will not accept interchangeable lenses. The need for this facility leads us directly to the camera that may be regarded as the single biggest development in post World War II photographic history – the single lens reflex.

The ability of a camera to take interchangeable lenses – so that, for example, the photographer can record extensive constellations at one extreme and high-quality 'close ups' of the Moon at another – may not be regarded as a *sine qua non* in the same way as the 'B' shutter function, but it does enable one to explore most areas of astrophotography.

Moreover, the versatility of the SLR and the fact that the best models are the basis of an entire system of photography that can accommodate the increasing skill and interest of the enthusiast make them the optimum choice for the astrophotographer. Medium format SLRs (those that use 120 or 70mm film) are available as well as 35mm models, but since they are regarded for the most part as cameras for professional use this discussion will concentrate on 35mm models.

It may be that some readers of this book are contemplating buying a camera. There are at least three options depending on the money available. The first is one of the lower-priced SLR models that offer a reasonable number of the features available on the more expensive models. Such cameras are usually robustly built and may normally be regarded as the next step for the budding photographer. Various models in the Zenith range and the somewhat higher-priced Pentax K1000 are current examples. A second option is to buy a used model of one of the leading makes from a reputable dealer. You need to select carefully, but in this way an excellent camera with most of the features needed, plus an extensive range of lenses and other items, can be obtained at a cost considerably below that of a new one.

The third possibility is to buy new one of the latest models from the leading manufacturers such as Nikon, Minolta, Canon, Pentax, Olympus, Leica and so on. Apart from price, an important difference between the first option and the second – though to a lesser degree – and the third, is the increased number of features and, therefore, greater versatility. (Clearly there will be differences of quality between the cheaper and more expensive models too – although this may not always be readily apparent.) The choice is one for the individual and must reflect personal circumstances. There is, however, one encouraging aspect, whatever choice is made: although you may have astrophotography very much in mind, these cameras are suitable for most forms of photography so that they are likely to be used extensively. And, should you decide, regrettably, to give up astrophotography or photography altogether, the popularity of good cameras means that there is a ready market for them.

Automatic exposure systems exist in many of today's cameras but effectively they play no part in astrophotography. The nature of most astronomical objects is such that automatic exposure systems cannot cope with them. (Hence the reference above to the suitability of older, manually operated, cameras.) One other feature of many current cameras is a dependence to a greater or lesser degree on battery power more especially the operation of the shutter. This is an important consideration, because often, you will use long exposures and continual use of the 'B' shutter speed will drain batteries faster than normal shutter speeds. Some very advanced and successful camera models – Minolta, for example – are totally dependent on battery power for all systems.

Such dependence on batteries creates a phobia in the minds of some photographers about the total failure of a camera at a critical moment (another facet of Spode's Law). This fear is exaggerated, because all that is required is care in ensuring that spare batteries of the right type are always carried. In any case, some models offer a flexibility in shutter operation. The Canon F1N, for example, has an electromechanical hybrid shutter mechanism in which the 'B' setting can be mechanically operated without battery power, and the Nikon F3 has a mechanical shutter release which also provides a time-exposure capability. The Pentax LX is somewhat different: it offers a hybrid system involving both electromagnetic and mechanical shutter operation, but, whereas 'B' is mechanically set and can be used without battery power, if the battery is present in the camera it is drained while the shutter is open. Clearly, a detailed review of this subject is not possible here but it is a point worth considering.

The mechanical or non-battery operation of the 'B' shutter setting should not be confused with manual operation of a camera's exposure controls – that is, the ability to switch from an automatic to a manual exposure mode. Most moderately priced to expensive 35mm SLR cameras have this essential facility.

There are a number of camera features which, although not absolutely necessary, are highly desirable. In everyday photography, the 35mm SLR is typically used at eye level, with the subject being viewed through a pentaprism. In general this is a comfortable position for the photographer and involves no strain. An important item of equipment for the astrophotographer, however, is a tripod that can be extended, usually to about a metre or so. The camera can then be pointed at varying angles towards the sky. This means, however, that you have to bend to view the scene through the pentaprism, the more so as the camera is aimed directly overhead. Tall individuals and those with any back problems will be more vulnerable – and some means of

viewing the sky by looking down towards the camera deck (just as an astronomer uses a star diagonal at the telescope) is a great advantage for all astrophotographers.

What is possible will depend on different camera systems. On some cameras where the standard pentaprism cannot be removed, right-angle finders can be fitted. These have an inevitable effect on the amount of light being transmitted to the eye. More preferable are various forms of right-angle viewers, which replace the normal pentaprism. These can be as relatively simple as what is normally called a waist-level finder (whereby one's eye looks down to the camera viewing screen via a small magnifier which facilitates focusing), to more complex units which afford greater magnification with individual eyesight adjustment. The system chosen must depend on camera type and money available, but both back and eyes benefit from the use of such a viewer and the results achieved can only be better. One feature of many right-angle viewers that may be a little disconcerting at first is that they reverse a scene laterally – i.e. from left to right. This can make the task of newcomers trying to find their way among the constellations just a little more difficult.

Also desirable is the ability to change from the normal viewing screen supplied with an SLR to one more suitable for astrophotography, because focusing at sometimes very low light levels can be difficult, particularly when long lenses (and telescopes) are used. The screen pattern and central range-finder disc on many everyday viewing screens serve no purpose in astrophotography. But two interchangeable screens are of value. When starting out – where constellations and stars will be the most frequent subjects – an overall and

The advantages and disadvantages of using lenses 'wide open'. These two pictures are of Andromeda (with Alpheratz in the Square of Pegasus at the extreme right), Cassiopeia (towards the top left) and the upper part of Perseus (with the double cluster or Sword Handle clearly seen) on the left. Exposure (a) was for twenty seconds on Kodak Recording Film 2475 (ISO1000), using a Nikkor 35mm f/1.4 lens at maximum aperture on a fixed camera. Many stars (and M31) are recorded, but coma is a problem as is the background 'fog' resulting mainly from light pollution. Stopping the lens down to f/2.8 and exposing for the same amount of time (b) greatly reduces the sky 'fog' and coma, but only the brightest stars in the three constellations are recorded.

A

B

A

These two images are of the Cygnus and Lyra
region of the summer sky which incluces the Milky
Way. Lyra (with the brilliant Vega) is towards the
right edge of the frame and the 'northern cross' of
Cygnus fills much of the middle. This comparison
is basically the same as the previous pair of images,
but the exposure was for thirty seconds each. Stars
abound in (a) but both Deneb and Vega are badly
overexposed with the latter affected by coma,
problems not suffered in (b). This length of
exposure, however, even with the short focal
length of wide-angle lenses, runs the risk of resulting in some star trailing when using a fixed camera.

B

uninterrupted fine-ground matt screen is most suitable. In tackling subjects at high magnifications, like the Moon or planets, a screen with a centre clear spot and a cross hair for use in parallax focusing is an advantage. The eye is moved very slightly from right to left and back again – and if the cross hair stays in the same position relative to the subject then the latter is in focus. This technique takes some getting used to but is very effective when mastered.

Two other camera features are valuable when working at slow shutter speeds. As will be seen later and in Chapter 5, lengthy exposures of a few seconds or more present no problem, since the black card technique is used. But between such lengthy exposures and very fast ones is a 'no man's land' where the results are highly vulnerable to camera shake and vibration. In these cases, the facility to lock the SLR mirror (which creates some vibration when it flips out of the light path before the shutter is opened) is most useful. The self timer (or delayed action release) is also valuable in that it removes the possibility of actions by the photographer causing the camera to shake, even when using a cable release.

Such features may seem somewhat esoteric to some but they can affect the quality of results. Most top-quality cameras have them and anybody planning a purchase with astrophotography in mind should be aware of the possibilities, though personal circumstances may well limit the options. Nor does this exhaust the list. Many cameras now offer slower, manually set shutter speeds in the range from one second through to eight and beyond, up to a norm of thirty seconds. This reduces the emphasis on using the 'B' setting. A few cameras (such as the Nikon F3) have a 'T' setting which performs the same function as 'B' but does not require the use of a cable release: the shutter is fired and stays open until the shutter speed ring is rotated to another value. Other cameras have a switch that enables the double-exposure prevention device to be overridden, which is helpful in multi-exposure images of the Moon and Sun. Data backs, which print the date or reference numbers on frames are growing steadily more popular – and, while normally costing a little extra, the choice of a totally black finish to the camera is well worth while because it helps to suppress reflections whether one is photographing at night, or perhaps copying originals.

Lenses

Just as it is possible to give only limited guidance on camera choice, so it is for lenses. In the final count it is the picture that a lens helps to create which is the crucial test of its suitability – and that test involves a combination of other factors (film, exposure, conditions and so on) which can either enhance or limit the quality potential of any lens. With this in mind, it is possible to offer some general observations on the lens in astrophotography.

Astrophotography presents what is arguably the most severe test possible for a lens. All lens systems have potential aberrations which designers endeavour to limit by means of compromises which vary according to the type of lens. Astrophotography tends to press these compromises to the limit. During the early attempts at photographing the stars, we endeavour to 'snatch' pictures by using very fast films with fast lenses set at their maximum aperture. When an ordinary photographer uses the lens in this way the picture may well be of a night or available light scene containing varying blocks of light and shade, and probably 'busy' subject matter, to draw the eye. Lens aberrations will be scarcely noticed.

In a constellation image, however, there is only dark sky and points of light – and any distortions will be revealed very clearly. In using a fast lens for star photography there is almost certain to be some coma (in which points of light become comet shaped) and possibly vignetting (a darkening of the image) – both occurring more particularly towards the edges of the field of view. Also, most lenses in everyday photography yield their best performance when stopped down two or three stops from full aperture – whereas the astrophotographer almost always wants maximum speed. One or two lenses – such as Nikon's 58mm f/1.2 Noct-Nikkor – have been designed for optimum correction of coma but they are expensive and few and far between. So, for the most part, we have to make the best of what are often excellent products which are used in the most disadvantageous way.

A second observation is a corollary of the one just made. In reviews of a lens, it may be stated that laboratory tests showed the lens capable of resolving so many lines per millimetre (one of the recognized performance standards). That information is worth knowing but we must remember that the lens is not going to be used in optimum circumstances, and certainly not in a laboratory, when devoted to astrophotography. We need to know about such factors as flare and edge definition when used at maximum aperture rather than an 'empty' performance under ideal conditions – although all these factors may point to the same conclusion.

Over the past decade or so the Japanese in particular have developed a flourishing industry of independent lens manufacturers (as distinct from camera manufacturers making their own products). Newcomers to photography always ask advice about this matter since the independents' prices are usually lower. Generalizing is difficult but I feel that in the main 'we get the lenses that we pay for' though the differences may not be readily apparent. In general use, the optical performance of a lens designed and made by a leading camera manufacturer may not seem to differ from that of an independent. But it is more than likely that the mechanical strength of the former's lens will be superior (and therefore able to withstand rougher treatment) and that optically it will have the edge when used under the most demanding circumstances – which astrophotography certainly creates.

More specific suggestions can be made about the most suitable focal lengths for use in astrophotography. Assuming that you will start by recording the constellations, a 'normal' focal length of 50mm – which the beginner is already likely to have – is perfectly satisfactory, though a somewhat wider-angle lens of around 35mm will be needed for more extensive constellations. Notwithstanding the aberrations, the lenses should be as fast as possible. At the other extreme, photography of the Moon and Sun really demands longer focal lengths, and a 500mm mirror-reflex lens, which is smaller and lighter than conventional designs, is an admirable starting point – even if it is of fixed aperture.

Tripod and Cable Release

There is an old photographic saying that a camera should never be handheld at a shutter speed slower than the reciprocal of the focal length of the lens in use. This is a rather involved way of stating that if you are using a 200mm focal length lens you should place it on a tripod at any shutter speed slower than $\frac{1}{250}$ of a second (the nearest to $\frac{1}{200}$). Given this sound advice it follows that astrophotography will almost always demand the use of a firmly placed tripod.

It is not a question of *any* tripod. The lengthy time exposures often used and the risk of camera shake and vibration from various sources necessitate a solid tripod with legs that can be locked firmly in position and in which there is the minimum of whip or movement. Modern light-weight tripods are convenient for carrying around and are satisfactory for meeting the demands of everyday photography, and with extreme care they may be used for constellation photography (i.e. with lenses of short focal length),

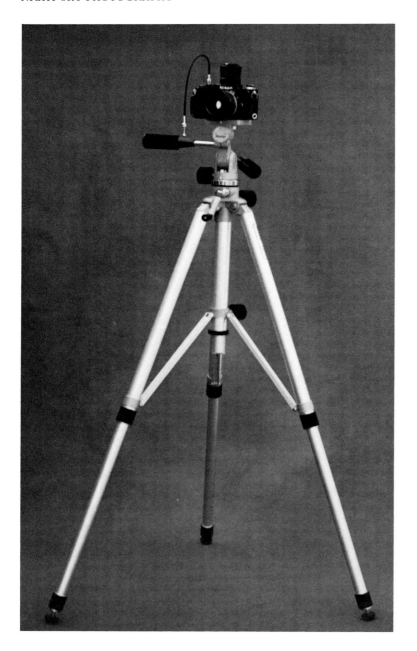

(Left) The fixed camera and a firm, 4kg (9lb) tripod. Many popular tripods are too flimsy to satisfy the exacting demands of astrophotography. A lightweight unit may be attractive because it is easy to pack and carry, but the astrophotographer frequently uses much longer time exposures than other photographers and such exposures demand a very firm and steady (and therefore usually heavy) tripod.

(Opposite above) The single lens reflex camera (SLR), besides being an admirable general purpose camera, is well suited for astrophotography. The more advanced camera systems have features which, although not essential, are desirable. The camera on the left, for example, is fitted with the normal, eye-level viewing prism: when the camera is being used on a tripod for astrophotography this can result in the photographer having to bend a great deal to see what is in the viewfinder. A right-angle, high magnification viewfinder—as in the camera on the right—is much more convenient although by no means inexpensive.

(Above) **At two extremes: the astrophotographer has need of lenses with greatly differing focal lengths. The 35mm f/1.4 at right—weighing about 400g—has a picture angle of 62° and is often used for photography of constellations. The 1000mm f/11 catadioptric lens—weighing almost 200g— has a picture angle of only 2°30′ and is an admirable lens for photography of the Moon and Sun (the latter through a special filter).**

but the use of longer focal lengths and of the 'in between' shutter speeds demands heavier tripods. While it may not exactly be a portable item, if an old-fashioned, professional, heavy tripod can be found at a reasonable price then buy it immediately.

One detail should be checked when purchasing a tripod, whether old or new. When the camera is fixed to the tripod, is it possible to angle the platform on which it is located so that the lens points directly upwards? This facility will be needed from time to time and various handles and other projections on some designs of tripod make it very difficult or impossible to aim the camera at an elevation of ninety degrees. If a tripod is otherwise satisfactory the problem can be overcome by the use of a heavy-duty ball-and-socket head but it is obviously an advantage if this further item is not required.

Various types of cable release are available (although you will not need one if the camera has a 'T' shutter setting). They differ chiefly in the manner in which the cable is locked, the size of the plunger head, and the length. The release is one item which is an essential for the astrophotographer, but yet is not costly – a pleasant change.

The ordinary photographer, particularly if an enthusiast, is likely to use filters quite frequently. It is my experience, however, that they play a far more limited rôle in the early stages of astrophotography, although they come into greater prominence later (in extreme focal length photography of the planets, for example). At this stage, it is a sound policy to regard a filter as constituting just two extra surfaces through which already limited light has to pass and, therefore, as something with which we should dispense.

43

Non-photographic Items

In the early years of photography there was no sophisticated shutter mechanism. The sensitized paper or plate was so slow that the 'artist' used a lens cap or hat to uncover the lens for an exposure that ran into many seconds. For lengthy time exposures astrophotographers imitate the early pioneers, and a large black card, which may be cut from a photographic paper box or something similar, is used. The technique is elaborated in Chapter 5.

A white-light torch is useful for checking one's site for obstructions before a session and to make sure nothing is being left behind afterwards – another point elaborated in Chapter 5. The provision of a red-light torch needs a little more explanation. In working around our camera, altering its controls and making notes, we need some light. The light from an ordinary torch would appear blindingly bright to our eyes and ruin their adaptation to the darkness, whereas the dark-adapted eye is least sensitive to red light. So, while a red-light torch supplies sufficient light for the astronomer's or astrophotographer's needs, it does not affect dark adaptation or at least does so only minimally. Specialist stores sell red-light torches but it is easy enough to locate a piece of dark red plastic about the house or toolshed. Rear cycle lights are not recommended: they are most efficient for their purpose on the bicycle but tend to be too powerful for our purpose.

The use of an electronic timer – as opposed to a watch – for timing long exposures carefully is a matter of personal choice. The advantage of the countdown timer of the type used in kitchens or photographic darkrooms is that the (usually) LCD time display is easily set by keys or some other means and an alarm is sounded at time zero. Watches tend to be somewhat smaller and more difficult to operate particularly in the dark and when fingers are beginning to get cold.

Finally there is the notepad and pen which are regarded so highly by astrophotographers. No guidance is needed on the former but some of the generally available ball point and other pens deal poorly with the task of writing on paper that becomes damp in the night air. A plastic cover could be used to prevent this but I have found at least two types of pen that write satisfactorily on damp paper – the Fisher pressurized cartridge pens, as used for many years by flight crews in the American space programme, and fine-point Pentel Ceramicron pens from Japan. Doubtless there are others.

CHAPTER FOUR

Films

Today the amateur has a very wide range of high-quality colour transparency, colour negative and black and white films from which to choose. In this chapter colour transparency and black and white films only are dealt with as being those most likely to be used by the newcomer to astrophotography. The versatility and quality of colour negative films is continually improving, but in photographing astronomical objects major assumptions have to be made about the colour of the original object when making a colour print from a masked negative, and the whole procedure may be regarded fairly as the province of the more advanced worker and therefore outside the scope of this book.

Colour Transparency Films

In Chapter 2 the point was stressed that astrophotography is 'another world' – and nowhere is this more the case than with films. Almost without exception, the films used by the amateur astrophotographer have been designed for normal use and for the reproduction of typical, everyday scenes – such as flowers in the garden or people's faces – though obviously the faster films are meant for occasions when the light level is lower. As a result, the films are manufactured to produce their best results in recording the multiplicity of everyday scenes and not the frequently exotic objects that are the astrophotographer's target. One important aspect of this difference is the way in which the films are tailored to be used at shutter speeds which fall broadly within the extremes from $\frac{1}{10}$ to $\frac{1}{1000}$ of a second. As will be seen in the following chapters, some astronomical subjects can be photographed at such speeds but many cannot and this introduces an important problem

– reciprocity failure – that will be discussed a little later, and mentioned quite frequently thereafter.

In choosing films for astrophotography there is a constant temptation to select materials which are very sensitive to light – 'fast' films in the jargon. Often such films are a necessity, for example when photographing constellations with a fixed camera. Where subjects do not require very fast films in the ISO1000 range, however, a slower film should be selected. (ISO stands for International Standards Organization: the higher the number, the faster the speed of the film. The value is the same as the ASA rating that was used until a few years ago.) The reason is a simple one – all things being equal, slower films yield better quality than faster films, and pictures exposed on them will be of higher definition and less grainy.

The principal film manufacturers – including such names as Kodak, Agfa, Fuji and 3M (Scotch) – offer an extensive range of films. Those up to ISO100 in speed can be described as slow, and are characterized by very high quality, good colour saturation and lively contrast (i.e. differences between the density of shadow and highlight areas). Their use in astrophotography is limited to those subjects where light is abundant – for example, the Sun or full Moon. Films up to ISO400 are now described as of medium speed and are used where light is at somewhat more of a premium (e.g. when photographing the crescent Moon). The quality of these films is still high but, because of their increased speed, grain is a little more obtrusive in the images, resolution is lower, and they are less contrasty. The third group of films has been introduced in relatively recent years and

attains claimed speeds of 1000, 1600 and even ISO3200. The far greater sensitivity to light they offer is at the expense of yet lower resolution and contrast, and results in higher graininess as well as what might be described as 'background noise' ('fog' in photographic terms, which is the inherent density found in an unexposed but developed film). These are the films which newcomers to astrophotography will typically use when photographing constellations with a fixed camera while trying to avoid star trailing caused by rotation of the Earth.

In general, the slow- and medium-speed films are exposed using shutter speeds not too dissimilar from those of ordinary photography. But where they and the ISO1000 plus films are exposed for periods longer than a second, then reciprocity failure must be allowed for. Theoretically, similar amounts of light should affect a film in the same way whether the light arrives over a short or a long period of time (i.e. half the amount of light supplied for twice the amount of time should have the same effect as twice the amount of light over half the time). This is known as a linear effect. Unfortunately it does not work like this with photographic film, and low-intensity reciprocity failure (we have no need to worry about the high-intensity form) results in lengthy exposures having to be far longer than expected.

Manufacturers tend to supply more data about reciprocity failure for their black and white materials than for colour. Thus Kodak recommends no compensation down to shutter speeds of $\frac{1}{10}$ of a second when using a wide range of its black and white films, but exposures thereafter have to be compensated for. In the case of an indicated exposure time of 100 seconds, either the aperture should be opened by three stops or the duration of the exposure increased to 1200 seconds – that is, increased from less than two to as much as twenty minutes.

Colour film suffers from a major additional difficulty with lengthy time exposures in that it basically comprises three layers that are sensitive to the three primary colours – red, blue and green. These are carefully balanced over the normal exposure range but once that range is exceeded the balance can break down and the colours produced in a final transparency go wildly astray. This is why manufacturers do not recommend the use of many of their colour products for exposures in excess of one, or at most ten, seconds – and only a few give positive guidance on the compensation for exposures lasting 100 seconds, which is quite short by astrophotographical standards. An example of the latter is ISO400 Ektachrome, where a 100-second exposure time should be accompanied by a two-and-a-half stop increase as well as correction with a cyan (blue-green) filter to compensate for colour shift.

This may begin to sound forbidding, but in practice experience teaches that at least some of the films perform well and indeed far better than we have any right to expect when subjecting them to circumstances for which they were not designed. The exposures likely to suffer from the effects of reciprocity failure are those of a few seconds – as in coverage of lunar eclipses or aurorae, for example – and those lasting many seconds or, when using a manual guider (discussed in Chapter 8), some minutes – as when photographing constellations. The former are not likely to be frequent subjects to start with so you can rely on bracketing to achieve a satisfactory result. Constellation photography is another matter and here the leading high-speed films should be compared in relation to your equipment and the quality of the sky.

The test programme may be shaped according to the length of exposures indicated in Chapter 8 – stepped from, say, ten seconds through twenty and thirty seconds to one, five, ten, fifteen and thirty minutes. In exposures of this length there is little published information and we have to find our own way around the performances of the various films under *our* conditions. To unravel apparent differences in film speeds from the differing reciprocity characteristics is time consuming, but in fact is not necessary since in the end it is the films' effective speed and colour quality that we are judging one against the other. To a considerable degree the latter is a matter of subjective opinion at this early stage, although as experience is gained one's opinions on how well a particular film renders astronomical objects will become better informed.

A critical element in colour acceptability is the nature of a film's maximum density – that is, the unexposed areas in a transparency. This is normally referred to as D-Max for short. When designing a colour film, photoscientists are concerned mainly with achieving the best possible rendering of the individual colours. When combined together in an image, the colours may not integrate to a neutral black D-Max. This does not matter much in everyday pictures because on the whole we are not interested in shadows and do not look at them closely. But in a constellation picture exposed over a relatively short period of some seconds, and with a good-quality, dark sky unaffected by light pollution, the maximum density will appear over a large area as the sky between the stars. If there is any marked colour bias in the D-Max this will be obtrusive and even objectionable.

Four of the leading ISO1000-plus colour transparency films currently available are Kodak Ektachrome P800/1600 Professional, Fujichrome P1600D Professional, Agfachrome 1000RS Professional and Scotch (3M) 1000. The first two are basically slower-speed films customized for push processing (see below) to high speeds. The other two are normally processed for the speeds indicated.

I have not had sufficient experience with the Fuji material to comment, but I have found that, while the Scotch material (a very early leader in the high-speed colour film field) is extremely fast with standard processing, it has a greenish D-Max which is unacceptable. The Ektachrome film has a pleasant blue-black D-Max but, although rated at ISO1600, is noticeably slower than the Agfachrome, even though this is rated at a nominal ISO1000. A significant consideration here is that Kodak itself does not recommend use of Ektachrome P800/1600 for exposures of one second or longer, presumably because of poor reciprocity characteristics. The Agfachrome D-Max is slightly brown-black, which is acceptable, and because of this film's realistic speed rating I use it as my standard high-speed material. It is rated at the nominal ISO1000 and processed normally. I stress, however, that it is for the individual to undertake tests and to make a personal choice on the basis of those tests.

'Push processing' is much in vogue in colour slide photography generally – and astrophotographers are among its keenest proponents. An effective speed increase can be secured with transparency film by extending the first development (which develops the silver image). This arises from the fact that it is a reversal material which is processed first to a negative and then to a positive. In a reasonably exposed transparency the shadow densities are considerably less dense than the D-Max and the full density potential of the material is not used, because when projected the material would appear too dark. If, however, the film is exposed at double the nominal rating, more shadow detail (i.e. higher densities) is recorded. Because it is a reversal film, if the first development is then extended, all the exposed areas (including the shadow areas) are lightened – not darkened, as happens with a negative film. This effective speed increase cannot be achieved with black and white film, as will be discussed a little later.

(*Opposite above*) Star trails around the celestial pole are among the simplest yet most dramatic images that can be taken with a fixed camera. This is a thirty-minute exposure on ISO200 Ektachrome Professional film using an f/1.4 35mm Nikkor lens stopped down to f/2.8 to limit any airglow effect. The top of Teide, the highest volcano in the Canary Islands, adds power to the composition. Polaris scarcely appears to have moved but the extent of movement by the stars towards the edge of the frame is evident.

(*Opposite below*) The distinctive shape of the main figure of Orion is unmistakable even though the stars are trailing. This is a ten-minute exposure on

ISO200 Agfachrome Professional film, using the Noct-Nikkor 58mm lens at f/2.8 to limit any airglow. A very fast film is likely to be a disadvantage in this sort of situation since airglow (or any light pollution) will build up more quickly on the film. The orange of Betelgeuse compares sharply with the brilliant white of Rigel and the varying shades of whitish blue and blue of the other main stars. The Great Nebula M42 appears lilac on this film; other films render it slightly more reddish although as it is a dim, diffuse object which is moving across the film, the saturation is never very strong. Nonetheless, pictures like this afford a useful general representation of the colours of the stars.

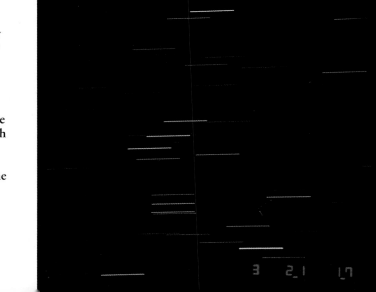

(*Left*) Local architecture in the Algarve provides an elegant foreground for this picture of a crescent Moon with Venus in the evening sky. ISO400 Fujichrome film was used, and a 35–105mm Nikkor zoom lens, that was being tested at the time, was found to be most useful for pictorial compositions of this kind. In addition an automatic exposure system was used, since there was no overpowering light source and an averaged meter reading of a twilight sky seemed valid. With aperture priority set at f/3.5, the system on the Nikon F301 gave an exposure of five seconds which worked well. Within a relatively few minutes the light level of the sky had fallen so far as to make an automatic exposure difficult if not impossible. Ideally, this sort of picture works best with a more slender crescent Moon. The star that can just be discerned to the west of and below Venus is Spica in the constellation Virgo.

(*Below*) The centre of our galaxy photographed from Australia in a four-minute exposure, using the camera guider illustrated on page 37. The lens was the 35mm wide-angle Nikkor at f/2.8 and the film was Agfachrome 1000RS Professional. There are three planets with numerous nebulae and star clusters in the field of view.

Once again, however, there is a price to pay: graininess increases, the colour balance can shift and because it is a reversal material extended development decreases contrast – which is often undesirable in astrophotography. None the less, it is an additional element which can be used to advantage in reducing lengthy exposure times. Moreover, I have found that in certain cases quality seems very little affected, such that when wishing to use an ISO400 rated film, I have used ISO200 Ektachrome in preference to the ISO400 equivalent and push processed it to achieve the higher speed rating. The resulting transparencies have been of at least equal quality to those produced by the higher speed transparency film.

The newcomer to astrophotography would be well advised to review the films available from the manufacturers in the different speed ranges. The reviews that appear in astronomy magazines are of value and can serve to reduce the list of films to be tested – but in the final count there is no substitute for direct experience. However, repeated chopping and changing between films is not wise because it usually means that the full potential of any single film is not established.

In considering the performance of colour films there is one point that needs to be made. Some astronomical objects may appear very different when photographed compared with their appearance to the eye. A classic example is the Great Nebula in Orion – M42. The light from emission nebulae of this type is confined largely to two narrow wavebands. One of these is near the peak sensitivity of the human eye which sees the nebula as a whitish or light bluish-green. This waveband falls between the peaks of the blue- and green-sensitive layers of colour film, but the other band, which is not seen well by the eye, records strongly on the red-sensitive layer. Hence the apparent discrepancy: we may choose which we prefer.

Black and White

Colour transparency film will doubtless appeal to many newcomers to astrophotography, but black and white film also has much to offer. Since the Moon is a monochromatic object it is best suited to black and white and extremely high-quality work can result. On the grounds of cost, black and white film is a sensible choice for meteor patrol work, recording the passage of satellites, and for early attempts at constellation photography, where there is no need to proceed beyond the negative stage in order to assess progress.

The same basic characteristics with regard to speed ratings apply as with colour transparency film. Slow films of ISO100 and below are fine grained and yield high resolution, quite high contrast and low fog. By comparison, the highly popular category of ISO400 films – such as Kodak Tri-X and Ilford HP5 – have a somewhat coarser grain, lower resolution, lower contrast and higher fog level, but are none the less high-quality, versatile films. They are the 'work horses' of professionals and keen amateurs in general photography, and demonstrate excellent exposure latitude – i.e. an ability to yield good-quality negatives despite some degree of over- or underexposure.

These ISO400 films are frequently push processed and photographers claim to have increased their speed by doing so. In fact, the speed of black and white material is fixed at the time of manufacture and no amount of manipulation of exposure or development can alter it – save that a $\frac{1}{3}$ stop safety factor, which most films incorporate, can be tapped, although this is so insignificant as to be scarcely noticeable. Unlike what happens with colour transparency film, the shadow densities of a black and white negative film exposed at its correct speed rating are only slightly denser than the fog level. If the film is exposed at a higher speed, underexposure occurs and that shadow detail is lost – in fact that part of the image no longer exists. While photography may appear to be a magical process, developing an image that no longer exists is impossible.

As to claims that push processing has increased a film's speed, all that has happened is that the photographer has sacrificed detail in the shadow areas of the picture either because they were not considered important or because the contrast of the original scene was so low (for example, under fluorescent lighting) that there were virtually no shadows anyhow. This does not constitute any increase in film speed and the push processing results in increased graininess, contrast and density overall, with overdeveloped highlights.

The use of ISO 100 and 400 black and white films for photographing the Moon – where relatively short exposures are used – does not touch on the need for push processing, and is discussed in Chapter 6. In considering time-exposure subjects such as constellations, reciprocity characteristics once again become an issue. Tri-X, for example, is one of the films for which Kodak advises very substantial increases whereby an indicated exposure of ten seconds is increased to fifty seconds (or two stops more), and an indicated exposure of 100 seconds is increased to 1200 seconds, or three stops more.

A sensible course of action is to repeat the series of exposures proposed for colour film at the standard speed of ISO 400. This will reveal the exposure times at which the various magnitude stars are recorded and whether the results are acceptable. Then another test should be staged rating Tri-X, HP5 or whichever film has been chosen, at ISO 800, and those results examined. Inevitably this becomes a game of swings and roundabouts because while the general increase in grain is a drawback the increase in contrast (with an underexposed sky and overdeveloped and brighter star points) might well be considered an improvement. In both cases, the films should be developed in a standard developer such as D76 or HC-110 (Dilution B) – or their equivalents.

For photographing satellites, where an exposure may last for perhaps thirty seconds, and during meteor patrols, where the shutter will be kept open for several minutes, it is doubtful whether anything is gained by push processing because the general increase in density and grain is likely to render any satellite or meteor trail less prominent. A useful experiment is to rate a film at its normal ISO 400 speed and to increase its contrast by the use of a high-contrast developer such as Kodak D19 or HC-110 (Dilution A).

The Tri-X type of film has been deservedly successful over many years. While careful tests are necessary, it may be that the appearance in 1986 of Kodak's T-Max films signified the arrival of products that will also be of great value for general-purpose photography of the sky. Doubtless other manufacturers will follow in due course.

The T-Max black and white films are based on the tabular grain concept that Kodak first introduced in its colour films. By providing a much larger surface area than conventional grains of the same mass, T-grains can adsorb large amounts of sensitizing dyes and other chemicals. The result, in short, is fast films with the qualities of medium-speed films in terms of grain and resolution, and medium-speed films with the image qualities of very slow films. Additional potential advantages in general astrophotography are that the contrast of the T-Max film is considerably higher than that of Tri-X, the fog level is lower and the reciprocity characteristics claimed are much better. Thus, using T-Max 400, a nominal 100-second exposure need be increased to only 250 seconds (one fifth of the Tri-X exposure time) or the aperture opened by one-and-a-half stops (compared with three stops). I am currently testing the two films that have been released (T-Max 100 and T-Max 400) and they show considerable promise.

Kodak Technical Pan 2415 Film is widely used by astrophotographers, but mainly for deep-sky photography of dim objects with the telescope, which is beyond the scope of this book. A brief reference to the film, however, is made in Chapters 6 and 12.

It is appropriate to end this somewhat wide-ranging review with two pieces of practical advice. When colour transparency film is used and the film is sent for commercial processing, it is vital to remember that laboratories have little experience of astrophotographs and their appearance – particularly if constellations are the subject. In that case it will be difficult for the operators to distinguish film frame edges, and the hard-won images may be returned inadvertently cut in two. I recommend two policies: either request that the film be returned uncut and unmounted (and carry this operation out personally) or shoot one or two ordinary scenes at the beginning of the film so that the cutting and mounting machine may be synchronized correctly. (In addition, if you have rated the film at a higher speed, be sure to inform the laboratory.)

Secondly, although a large number of photographs of some subjects – such as an eclipse – will be taken over a very short period, it is quite likely in the early stages that a relatively small number of images (perhaps ten or so) will be taken at any one time. Most transparency films are of twenty-four or thirty-six exposure lengths so, unless you do not object to waiting for the entire film to be used up before seeing the results, it is a useful idea to contemplate cutting the film carefully into two or three sections and loading them into plastic reloadable cassettes, which are available at most retailers. It is easy enough to do if a darkroom or changing bag is available: alternatively, a specialist photodealer (for a small fee) or maybe a keen and well-equipped photographer friend might oblige. Of course, unless you do your own processing this will increase the cost of processing.

A twelve-exposure film with leader is around 55cm in length and an eighteen-exposure film 80cm in length. Make sure that the newly loaded film is wound the correct way: looking down at the long end of the spool, the film should be wound in a clockwise direction around the spool.

CHAPTER FIVE

Procedures

The chapters that follow concentrate on the photography of specific celestial objects. The manner in which a photographic session is prepared and then conducted does not differ greatly from subject to subject, so to reduce possible repetition in later chapters outline guidance is given here. Some of the comments may seem elementary but, taken as a whole, they constitute a sound basis upon which the inexperienced can conduct a session with good chances of success.

In the initial stages of astrophotography a vast amount of setting up is not required, so we may quite frequently take a chance on the weather. But there is a need to be realistic about the potential effect of wind speed when trying to photograph some targets. Long focal length lenses present a large area to the wind, and under windy conditions, photography of the Moon, for example (more especially at the slower shutter speeds used for crescent phases or, even worse, during lunar eclipses) is likely to lead to poor results even though the camera is mounted on a firm tripod. Quite moderate focal lengths can be affected over long time exposures and it is a sound general rule to regard windy conditions as being unsuitable for most forms of astrophotography. Of course, the decision is shaped by events: few astrophotographers would put their cameras away during a major event – such as a solar eclipse – simply because there was a strong wind blowing!

Astrophotography during the summer months can be a great pleasure (even if night scarcely falls at all) but winter returns all too quickly. No programme of astrophotography or observing can be carried out well if we are feeling very cold and the point needs to be made strongly that, even in the early stages, any idea of just 'popping out' into the garden for a few minutes to dash off one or two exposures is a prescription for misery and therefore failure. It will not be a few minutes and as the ill-dressed photographer gets colder so the chances of any success plummet.

When contemplating the first sessions in astrophotography it is a good idea to have an outline programme – even if it is a mental one, or just headings on a scrap of paper. Perhaps the aim is to photograph ten constellations over a couple of hours as they move close to zenith, or to experiment with various exposures of the Moon on black and white film to compare the results. It is wise, however, not to make the plan too complex or ambitious. Assume that things will always take longer than you think and plan ten exposures rather than fifteen or twenty. Have a reserve of targets so that more can be tackled if things go well.

Part of the planning should include consideration of the most efficient way of operating. For example, if the aim is to record a number of constellations with two different focal length lenses, it is easier to record each object using the two lenses before moving to the next – rather than leaving one lens mounted during a first sweep of the objects and then having to repeat the series of camera movements for the second sequence.

Whether the location initially chosen for photography is in the garden or farther afield, check during an earlier night that no lights will shine directly and continually into the camera lens (and during sessions ban all matches, lighters and white-light torches – other than your own – from the area). Finally, when you come to the actual photography, you need to follow good, sound everyday photographic practice: make sure the lenses are clean (because you need every particle of light there is); make sure, if you keep film in the freezer (which reduces to a minimum chemical changes which occur inevitably with age in a sensitized product), that you allow several hours for it to come up to room temperature before putting it in the camera, and make sure the film *is* being taken up by the film wind (you should see the rewind crank arm rotating if it is).

So – the evening is fair, the targets chosen and the spirit enthused. Check off the items required on a list: this may sound quite unnecessary but if your photographic location is some way from home and you arrive there without an important piece of equipment you will wish you had taken such a precaution.

1 Loaded camera – with one or two ordinary pictures already exposed at the beginning of the film; lens/lenses; lens hood; cable release.

2 Tripod.

3 Planisphere/star maps. (These will not be needed during photography of the Moon, for example, but are useful to have for identifying unknown objects.)

4 Timer; black card.

5 Red-light torch; white-light torch.

6 Pen; notebook – including notes on intended targets.

7 Reserves of expendables – batteries etc. – which means checking these reserves before the shops shut! (Include a second film in case the work goes extremely well, the evening continues fair and you are inspired.)

8 Although not essential, a small picnic table or broad-topped stool is useful as a surface on which to place items not in continual use and which may not fit in pockets – black card, planisphere, lenses (be careful!) and so on. A light-coloured surface facilitates finding the objects in the dark.

Before setting any equipment up on the chosen site, sweep the area (whether it is in the garden or elsewhere) with the white-light torch for any obstructions which in the dark could prove dangerous – or at least ruin an exposure as you trip and knock the tripod over. The white-light torch should not be used again until the session is concluded. Full dark adaptation of the eyes can easily take an hour or so.

The method of proceeding during a series of exposures does not differ greatly other than in the extremes of shutter speed that can be used. In the check list that follows a fast film is being used for constellation photography, with a standard shutter speed of twenty seconds:

1 Set the shutter speed to 'B'. Set the aperture to maximum. Focus the lens on infinity. (Some people then tape the rings at these positions to prevent any accidental alteration.) Check that the camera/tripod combination is firm and locked. Set the timer to a chosen duration (twenty seconds).

2 Locate the object visually. Frame it in the viewfinder. (Remember that if a right-angle viewer is in use, often the image is reversed from left to right – which can take some getting used to when trying to frame constellations.)

3 Place the black card in front of the lens but not touching it. Fire the shutter with the cable and lock it. Wait two or three seconds for vibrations to dampen and then remove the card carefully without touching the lens. Simultaneously start the timer. (Locking or unlocking the cable release while holding the card requires dexterity. Some cables make locking easier by not using a threaded nut but a disc which is rotated in advance in one direction so that when the plunger is pressed the cable locks automatically. This still leaves the problem of unlocking the cable – an action requiring two hands – while holding the card in front of the lens. The presence of a third hand is an obvious help. For relatively short exposures such as the twenty seconds suggested here, you can experiment with firing the cable release and holding the plunger down rather than locking it. There is a risk of camera movement if the cable does not have slack, but with care it can work. The technique should be judged on the results. If the camera has a 'T' setting a cable release is not required – an obvious advantage.)

4 Hold the card ready well to one side of the lens as you endeavour to observe the area of sky appearing in the photograph.

5 The timer sounds. Place the card in front of the lens immediately. Unlock the cable release to end the exposure and place the card to one side. Cut the timer alarm and reset it to twenty seconds using the red-light torch if the timer does not have an LED display. Wind the film on.

6 Make notes on exposure. The bulk of the notes can be written in advance but any changes should be carefully recorded – in addition to observations made during the

exposure, e.g. aircraft, meteor, satellite and so on. With a programme like this there is no need to cover up the lens during the passage of an aircraft and recalculate the exposure time. It is simpler just to repeat the exposure.

7 Check the front of the lens for condensation (see page 60). Take care not to breathe when close to the viewfinder or the lens, because condensation will occur immediately.

8 Check that the aperture setting is as required, that the shutter speed is still on 'B' and that the focusing distance is on infinity.

9 Return to step 2 and repeat the sequence.

The shutter speed chosen for the above star images was long enough not to present problems when using the black card technique. But we need to consider as well the other extreme of very fast shutter speeds – as used in photography of the full Moon or Sun. The ideal here is to use a camera in which the mirror can be locked up (to remove another source of vibration) and a self timer to release the shutter after a delay (thereby reducing any slight camera movement created by the pressing of the shutter release cable). The delay that results when you use the self timer lasts for several seconds; it can be omitted if an exposure is time critical – which is only likely to happen in advanced astrophotography. If the camera does not have one or both of these features then there is still a very good chance of satisfactory exposures if the shutter speeds are high – say $\frac{1}{250}$ of a second and upwards – despite the use of long lenses.

The major risk of camera shake and vibrations causing smeared images arises with critical shutter speeds ranging from, say, $\frac{1}{60}$ of a second to about one second or so. These are the speeds used for crescent phases of the Moon, eclipses and some conjunctions, and the problem is compounded by the likely use of long focal length lenses. Our reactions are nowhere near quick enough to use the black card at the faster end of this range and it is unlikely that its use will prove very satisfactory at the longer end (our actions occupy too great a proportion of the brief exposure) even though it must be attempted. One small advantage here, however, is that locking the cable is clearly not necessary (nor possible).

Once again, there is little danger of vibration when using a sophisticated camera that features not only a mirror lock but also a self timer. Such cameras usually have pre-set shutter speeds in the range of one, two, four and eight seconds (if no higher), so the shutter can be set to these values with 'B' not being required. It is a different matter for cameras without these features. In the absence of a mirror lock and a self timer, the use of a bulb (or pneumatic) shutter-release cable should be considered because it subjects the camera to less physical movement than the conventional cable. Another possibility is just to make the most of the opportunities that do exist – such as ensuring that the tripod is rock-steady, choosing wider apertures to get faster shutter speeds, or possibly choosing a faster film (with somewhat inferior grain characteristics) to achieve even faster shutter speeds. Where shutter speeds of one or two seconds are required and are not available as pre-set speeds on the camera, then you will have to practise with the black card and gain as much proficiency as possible. It is impossible to generalize and there are no simple solutions, but something will have been achieved if you have been alerted to the problems in this speed range – more especially when long lenses, which exaggerate any smear in images, are being used. The best policy is to experiment and to establish the best-quality results that can be achieved by adopting various procedures.

The check list above can be modified for shorter exposures but I have not elaborated on it here because the steps will differ according to the features of the camera in use. If you feel the need you can draw up your own list.

Some detailed advice concerning the end of the session is pertinent. Check that the final exposure has been terminated and that notes have been completed. (Never trust to memory!) Although you may not have been using the camera's exposure meter system (if it has one), it may be activated: if it does not cut out automatically after a set period, switch it off now. At this stage the dark adaptation of your eyes ceases to be important. Switch the white-light torch on and check that all the items of equipment, maps, cards and so on have been gathered safely together. Whether in the garden at home or miles away sweep the photography site with the torch to make sure nothing is being left behind.

When the equipment is taken from cold, outside temperatures into a warm room, condensation takes place immediately on all exposed surfaces. (The notepaper will have dampened anyway during the session; at home lay the sheets out separately so that they do not stick together as they dry.) It is best not to try and wipe the surfaces of most of the equipment but to leave them to dry in their own time overnight. The condensation probably does no harm but it is easy to feel a little unhappy about expensive cameras and lenses

being subjected to such treatment. There is, however, a straightforward way of preventing it – a large, clear plastic bag with a ribbed seal along the top, or even a plastic lunch box, which is large enough to take the camera and lenses.

While still outdoors the camera with lens fitted is placed in the bag or box which is then sealed. The camera can now be brought inside. Condensation immediately forms on the *outside* of the container but not on the equipment inside. It takes some time for the temperatures to balance, and unless there is extreme urgency about the results it seems sensible to leave the camera and lens inside the container until the morning.

It is sound practice to get into a set routine on when to remove the film from the camera. Either rewind the film immediately after ending the last exposure, extract it from the camera and place it in a film can, or, after rewinding carefully, leave the film in the camera until the morning when both are removed from the plastic container.

The next day, or as soon as possible, all equipment should be checked and non-optical surfaces wiped over with a soft, clean cloth. Use a lens brush/air puffer to remove any dust from the inside of the camera or – if you do use one of the aerosol cans of air – be very careful that you hold it upright and do not direct a powerful blast of air from a short distance straight at the focal plane shutter.

Most important of all, check the back and front elements of the lenses that were used during the previous night's session. Because the back element is protected by the camera body when fitted, it should rarely need attention, but dust, dirt and fingerprints can all too easily affect the front element. First, hold the lens upside down and use a blower brush to remove as much dust as possible. Take a lens tissue (not a spectacle-cleaning tissue, which usually contains silicone and can damage the surface and coatings of photographic lenses), fold it in half several times and apply one or two drops of lens-cleaning fluid to the centre of the pad. Starting at the centre of the lens and holding the tissue at the edges, wipe in a circular motion outwards. You may need to repeat this with a new tissue, but never apply lens-cleaning fluid direct, because it could seep around the edges of the lens and into the lens barrel. As a test of how clean the lens element is, breathe on it. If the condensation evaporates evenly as a gradually diminishing circle the lens is clean; if patches or spots show up in the condensation – start

again. When all is well, replace the UV filter (if you fit one) and the rear and front lens caps. The camera is then ready to use for the next session.

The way in which you make notes for a photographic session is a matter of personal choice. There is no need to design what amounts to a form but the following contains most of the essential information. Some of the main heading information can be dropped into the column area if, for example, different lenses or f-numbers are being used. Also, if you move around you should note the location. The Exposure Began column is useful if – in the absence of a data back recording the time – an unexpected (and unobserved) event is recorded on the film:

Date:......	Camera:......	Lens:.....	Stop:......	Film:......
Subject		Exposure Began	Shutter Speed	Comments

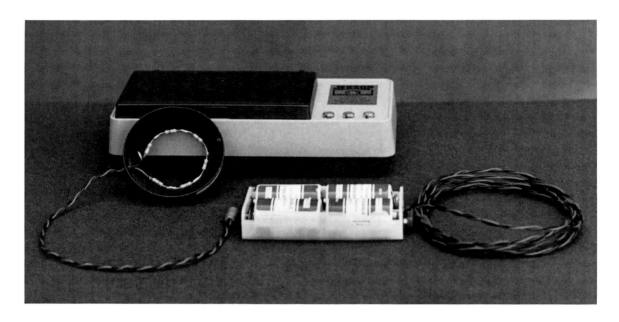

A six-resistor lens heater shown with battery pack and battery charger. The resistors nestle within a dedicated lens hood which fits all lenses with a standard 52mm front thread. The unit is switched on by simply joining the heater wire to the battery wire by means of connectors.

Combating Dew

When air cools and reaches the critical temperature known as dew point, water droplets condense on anything at or below the temperature. All too often, despite the use of a lens hood, this seems to be the front element of a lens.

A lens tissue can be used to remove the condensation but it will quickly re-form. A hair dryer used gently from a safe distance at intervals is effective (even during exposures, provided care is taken to keep out of the field of view of the lens), but most are powered from mains electricity, which may not be available. A battery-powered lens heater is an efficient way of providing just enough warmth to keep the temperature of the front element of the lens slightly higher than the surrounding air.

The illustration opposite shows a heater like this, that I have used. The minimum amount of heat required was estimated at 2 watts powered by 6 volts, and the resistance was calculated at 18ohms, according to the formula resistance = voltage squared/ wattage. The heater comprises a string of six $\frac{1}{2}$ watt 30ohm resistors in series to distribute the heat equally around the edges of the lens. A small hole was drilled through the side of a dedicated lens hood to take the wire from the power supply.

The amperage of an 18ohm resistance operating at 6 volts is 0.333amps or 333 milliamperes. (Ohm's Law tells us that the current in amperes equals voltage/resistance.) Various types of power supply can be considered but rechargeable nickel-cadmium batteries provide a safe and easily portable solution. I have found that a set of four 'C'-type rechargeable batteries (nominally 1.2v, 1.2Ah) will operate the heater for approximately six hours before recharging is required.

Materials

'C'-type battery holder with snap-on leads
Four 'C'-type, rechargeable, nickle-cadmium batteries
Universal battery charger
Length of electrical wire 16/0.2 gauge or similar. (About 2m/79in, which is long enough to allow the battery pack to be placed beneath a tripod out of the way, and is joined to about 20cm/8in of wire from the resistors/lens hood by a connector)
Six $\frac{1}{2}$ watt 30ohm resistors
Soldering iron and solder

CHAPTER SIX

The Moon

In terms of the exposures required, the Moon presents the easiest task of all for the newcomer to astrophotography, because it reflects light from the Sun — just as the Earth does. (The Moon does it very poorly — with an albedo of only 7 per cent compared with the Earth's 29 per cent — but the situation is directly comparable.) This means that you will sometimes find such comfortingly familiar exposures as $\frac{1}{250}$ at f/11 occurring. (Exposures will be discussed in detail a little later.) It is natural to think of using colour film when photographing the Moon, but it is essentially a monochromatic object and therefore a prime target for black and white film. This film also affords an opportunity to deal with some of the problems caused by extremes of lighting contrast on the Moon. Colour, however, does come into its own during lunar eclipses.

Although the exposures can be similar to those in everyday photography on Earth, the focal lengths required for effective photography of the Moon are very different. Relative to the Earth, the Moon is one of the Solar System's larger satellites, orbiting at a mean distance from us of more than 380,000km (237,500 miles). From Earth it has an angular size of a little more than half of one arc

Focal length is critical in obtaining useful photographs of the Moon. The full 35mm film frame has been enlarged to the same degree in each of the first four images *(opposite and overleaf)* which show the effects of using (a) 50mm, (b) 180mm, (c) 500mm and (d) 1000mm focal length lenses. The fifth image (e), taken with a 2000mm mirror-reflex lens, has been enlarged to fit the page. Film and processing was standard throughout but the last two frames were taken during a different full Moon period.

A

B

E

degree, much like the Sun. In terms of capturing it on film, this size is demanding. There is a useful formula for approximately establishing the image size of the Moon produced by a lens mounted on a 35mm camera – f(focal length)/100. This means very roughly that every 100mm of focal length will yield 1mm of Moon on the film. So our 'normal' 50mm lens will produce an image 0.5mm in diameter!

The meaning of this is demonstrated by the illustrations on the previous pages. Pictures of the Moon were taken with 50mm, 180mm, 500mm, 1000mm and 2000mm lenses and in the first four the full frames of the resulting images were enlarged by the same amount. While the Moon is extremely small even with enlargement, lunar maria can be distinguished in the image taken with the 50mm lens. These details are much clearer in the image obtained using the 180mm lens, where larger craters such as Tycho, in the southern hemisphere, are discernible. Numerous craters are apparent in the 500mm lens image and there are obvious, further gains when using the two longest lenses.

Although a major component, the lens is only one factor in producing an image, with film being another obvious component. Thus if we enlarge a 5mm-diameter Moon image five times and a 10mm-diameter image five times so that there is a fair comparison, it will be evident that the latter appears to be 'sharper' because the grain of the film is less obtrusive.

It is none the less true that a major reason for the better results obtained with the longer focal length lenses is their light-gathering capability – which means we are back again to considering lens diameters. If we limit the consideration entirely to the theoretical resolving power of the lenses, we can calculate their performances in arc seconds by the formula 114/d, where d is the diameter in millimetres. The 50mm f/1.8 lens has a diameter of almost 28mm with an optimum resolving power therefore of 4 arc seconds. The 180mm f/2.8 lens can resolve 1.78 arc seconds, the 500mm f/8 mirror lens 1.82 arc seconds, the 1000mm f/11 mirror lens 1.25 arc seconds and the 2000 f/11 mirror lens 0.63 arc seconds. Notice incidentally that it is not simply a question of focal length *per se*. The fast 180mm f/2.8 lens has a diameter of more than 64mm so has a better resolving power than the 500 f/8 with a diameter of 62.5mm. It is a question of lens diameter and light grasp.

Notwithstanding this, for good photography of the Moon there is no substitute for focal length (though reference will be made later to 'time lapse' images on a single frame made with shorter focal length lenses). With care in exposure and processing, a 200mm focal length lens will produce a worthwhile image. If, however, a focal length of 500mm can be used, then (all things being equal) the gains in quality are significant. Increasingly, ordinary photographers are applying their hobby to sports and bird watching – in both of which there is a premium on focal length – and the 500mm mirror lens in particular (because it is of such a compact design) is becoming popular. The power of shorter focal length lenses may be boosted, of course, by the use of teleconverters – though there is then a loss of speed.

Once again it has to be said that in using our long focal length lenses we are not 'getting something for nothing'. The Moon moves in

These two images demonstrate how constellation images can be taken in twenty seconds with fast lenses on ISO1000 film using a fixed camera. The lens used in both cases was the f/1.4 35mm wide-angle Nikkor and the film Agfachrome 1000RS Professional. The shape of Ursa Major (also known as the Plough or the Big Dipper) needs no introduction, but the location of the main stars well to one side is to accommodate the great expanse of the constellation which stretches beneath and beyond the dipper 'bowl' (a). Discrete hues of white, blue, and yellow can be distinguished quite easily among the stars although it is not as pronounced as with trailing. From the handle of the Plough downwards can be seen the smaller constellations of Canes Venatici and Coma Berenices. Notice that placing the main asterism or cluster of stars at the edge of the field of view exacts the penalty of coma, which distorts the shape of the main stars.

A

B

(*Previous page*, b) The constellation Centaurus can be regarded justly as the southern hemisphere's equivalent of Orion for grandeur. About two-thirds of the constellation can be seen moving westwards along the rim of the Circo de Las Canadas in Tenerife. The two pointers to the Southern Cross—Alpha and Beta Centauri—do not rise this far north but Omega Centauri, the brightest of all the globular star clusters, is plainly in view as a small yellowish disc just west of centre and about one quarter of the way up from the horizon. It can be located readily with the aid of a star map. Once again it deserves to be stressed how well the film has retained delicate colour differences.

(*Above*) Oncoming dawn and dark clouds frame the waning crescent Moon and Venus just as well as a foreground of interesting buildings or trees. The sky is still dark enough and the phase of the Moon slender enough for Earthshine to be recorded clearly. Venus appears to be entering the Hyades star cluster in Taurus, with the orange star Aldebaran prominent beneath it. A four-second exposure was given on Ektachrome ISO200 film using an 85mm Nikkor at f/2.8.

its orbit from west to east and, because of the Earth's rotation, appears to move from east to west each night. Alterations in the orbital velocity of the Moon complicate any calculations but on average it is moving eastwards in its orbit at 3476km/h (2172mph). Its apparent movement in the opposite direction as a result of the Earth's rotation is much faster – over 104,000km/h (65,000mph) or 29km (18 miles) per second. This works out at a little more than 15 seconds of arc per second of time.

We need to remember this since the longer the focal length (and the greater the magnification of the object) the greater the risk of the image 'smearing' in the photographs. Without going into too much detail, the same formula elaborated in Chapter 8 for securing essentially trail-free images of the stars is valid for the Moon: divide 700 (or 500 if we are being hypercritical) by the focal length of the lens, and the resulting figure is the exposure in seconds that will result in virtually no image movement using a fixed camera. So this threshold exposure is 1 second with a 500mm focal length lens and only $\frac{1}{4}$ second with a 2000mm focal length lens. But how feasible are such shutter speeds?

The Moon is an extended object which is seen with great variability through the Earth's atmosphere. Such variation is another reminder of how necessary it is to use suggested exposures as a basis of experimentation only. With the Moon we have the additional variation in exposure resulting from the phase angle of the Sun. For example, during the early lunar 'morning' (or late 'evening') when the Moon appears to us as a slender crescent, a longer exposure is required than when the Sun is overhead during the Moon's noontime, when it appears full to us.

The following exposures are a guide for your first attempts. It is essential to follow the good photographic practice that has already been stressed – particularly when the uncomfortable 'in-between' shutter speeds are indicated – and also to give at least one stop or one shutter speed more exposure on the one side and less on the other.

Moon Phase	ISO400 film	ISO100 film
Crescent	$\frac{1}{60}$: f/11	$\frac{1}{30}$: f/8
Quarter	$\frac{1}{250}$: f/8	$\frac{1}{60}$: f/8
Gibbous	$\frac{1}{250}$: f/11	$\frac{1}{125}$: f/8
Full	$\frac{1}{250}$: f/16	$\frac{1}{125}$: f/11

The two film speeds included here are considered to be the most suitable for black and white work but it is somewhat tedious to have to extrapolate the information to other films and/or other focal ratios. There is a convenient formula in which film speed and focal ratio give approximate shutter speeds in seconds. This is:

$$t = \frac{f^2}{s \times B}$$

where t is the time, f is the focal ratio, s is the film speed and B is a brightness value for the phase of the Moon. These values (which may be refined as you gain experience) are: Crescent: 20 (try 10 for a very slender crescent); Quarter: 40; Gibbous: 80; and Full: 200. It must be emphasized again that these values are provided to enable you to make a meaningful start so that film will not be wasted because of wildly inappropriate

The effect of film choice and developer is well demonstrated in these two images of the full Moon. (a) Kodak Technical Pan 2415 film was used here, rated at ISO100. The exposure using a 2000mm Nikkor mirror-reflex (f/11) was $\frac{1}{60}$ of a second. The film was developed in HC-110 (dilution D). Technical Pan is a high-contrast, high-resolution film which helps to deal with the blandness of the full Moon. The second image (b) was taken on T-Max 400 film using the 2000mm Nikkor with an exposure time of $\frac{1}{125}$ of a second. The film was developed conventionally in HC-110 (dilution B). Although T-Max has a lively contrast, this print obviously has a shallower contrast gradient than the first image. Printing skills are very important in making comparisons of this kind and it could be argued that the Technical Pan image should have been printed on a paper that was one grade softer. As it is, while in the original prints the Tech Pan image may appeal because of its greater liveliness, on careful study the information content of the T-Max image is revealed to be higher. The two images were separated by the passage of some five years. By chance they enable us to distinguish the effects of lunar libration (or wobbling of the

A

Moon on its axis): compare how close the Mare Crisium (the circular object at the top right of the disc) is to the limb in the two images. The difference is not enormous but we can see more of the eastern edge of the Moon in the second, T-Max image. Similarly, study of the dark crater Grimaldi, close to the south-west (lower left) limb of the Moon, reveals that it is predictably closer to the limb in the T-Max image, which means that we are seeing less of the western hemisphere.

B

exposures. But there are no universally correct answers – only those that work for each individual astrophotographer with a particular set of circumstances relating to equipment/film/processing and to atmospheric and lighting conditions.

Black and white film provides us with some flexibility in dealing with the contrast problems inherent in photographing the Moon. When it is full it is 'high noon' of the Moon's month-long day and night cycle. As on Earth, shadows are extremely short and it is difficult to distinguish objects. For the photographer

it is a bland object and you need to enhance what contrast does exist. To do this, within limits, you can pursue a method that will be known to the experienced black and white photographer. Contrast in a negative is controlled by development: therefore if you underexpose the Moon and overdevelop you should produce greater contrast and therefore a livelier image. About half a stop of underexposure and one third of overdevelopment should be the maximum, otherwise increased grain resulting from the overdevelopment will become obtrusive.

There is another way of tackling the blandness of the full Moon. One or two extremely versatile films exist that, with different developers, yield greatly different contrast characteristics. One of these is Kodak 2415 Technical Pan Film. This is a fine-grain film with extended red sensitivity that is used widely in astrophotography. Its value here is that whereas it can be exposed at a rating of up to ISO64 to yield negatives with a normal contrast index of up to about 0.70, it can be rated as high as ISO200 and then deliver a claimed contrast index of 2.50. This is a top-quality film which is well worth experimenting with in lunar photography, as well as with other subjects.

There is still the matter of the crescent moon, where the contrast problem is reversed. The subject is extremely contrasty and the chances of getting totally dark blacks and featureless highlights are high. Normally a higher speed film is used for photographing the crescent Moon because faster films tend to be less contrasty than slower ones. Wide latitude also helps to record detail in shadows and yet not lose detail entirely in the high-

Adjustments to exposures and development times can help with the control of contrast in the crescent Moon. The first image (a) *(opposite)* was exposed on Kodak Tri-X film for $\frac{1}{30}$ of a second using the Nikkor 2000mm mirror-reflex. It is a satisfactory image, but the surface towards the limb becomes steadily more 'washed out'. The film was developed conventionally in D76 diluted 1/1. The second image (b) *(right)* was taken on T-Max 400 but whereas the exposure of $\frac{1}{60}$ was standard the development time in D76 diluted 1/1 was cut by 25 per cent. This caused the detail in the terminator area to be less well delineated—but the highlight areas towards the limb have not developed so much and more detail is discernible. This was a useful experiment, but in comparing films the tests should be conducted under absolutely comparable conditions with the same tests being applied to each.

LUNAR ECLIPSE

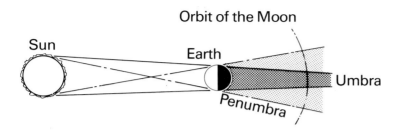

Orbit of the Moon
Sun
Earth
Umbra
Penumbra

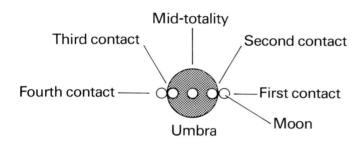

Mid-totality
Third contact
Second contact
Fourth contact
First contact
Umbra
Moon

The diagram on the left shows what causes a lunar eclipse, when the Earth moves between the Sun and the Moon. The three bodies are roughly in this alignment once a month (at the time of the full Moon), but the Moon's inclination of 5° to the ecliptic results in lunar eclipses very much less frequently than this. The second diagram shows the various stages of a lunar eclipse as the Moon moves though the Earth's shadow. The size of that shadow helps to explain why a lunar eclipse lasts much longer than a solar eclipse, which occurs when the much smaller Moon travels between the Earth and Sun.

lights. The technique here is the opposite of that when dealing with the full Moon: a degree of overexposure and a degree of underdevelopment to limit contrast – both by the same proportions as indicated for the full Moon. In both cases choice and manipulation of the most suitable printing papers contribute to an optimum result, so an experienced black and white darkroom worker is at an advantage.

Lunar Eclipse

A lunar eclipse may not have the drama of a solar eclipse but it is none the less a fas-

cinating experience to watch the Moon decline from its normal bright state to an orange-red or coppery hue at the height of the eclipse. Fascinating it may be but it sets the astrophotographer a sterner test than normal lunar images.

The diagram shows broadly what happens in a lunar eclipse. The period from when the Moon first touches the outer edge of the penumbra till it exits the penumbra on the other side can last for around six hours, but totality – when the Moon is totally within the umbra of the Earth's shadow – is a much shorter period of up to about one hour and forty minutes. When the Moon moves into the penumbra there is little difference compared with when it is normally lit by direct sunlight, but the situation changes imperceptibly. After first contact – when the Moon's leading edge, or limb, moves into the umbra – a broad line of shadow moves across the lunar surface until second contact, at which time the Moon passes wholly within the umbra. (When the Moon is partly in umbra and partly in penumbra, exposure has to be for one or the other since the film cannot handle both extremes of lighting at one time as is shown in the illustration on page 103.) Deepest darkness occurs quite logically at mid-totality following which third contact takes place as the Moon's leading limb begins to move out of the umbra. Fourth contact occurs when the Moon's trailing limb is just about to pass out of the umbra – and then the final penumbral stage begins.

Photography of the various stages of the eclipse is complicated by the relative brightness or darkness of the Moon during totality, its position in the sky, and atmospheric conditions at the photographer's location – all of which could affect exposures significantly. Although the Earth blocks off all direct sunlight from the Moon during totality, the lunar surface is not black but an orange, red or muted copper hue, depending on the state of the Earth's atmosphere, which refracts sunlight to create the effect. A lunar eclipse lasts much longer than a solar eclipse and a sight of it is not restricted (as during a solar eclipse) to a limited path on the Earth's surface for a brief time – it may be seen anywhere in the world where the Moon is up (and skies are clear!).

Yet again stressing that the contents are meant as a basic guide only, this table should help:

Eclipse Phase	Film speed ISO					
	64	100	200	400	1000	1600
Deep in penumbra	$\frac{1}{60}$: f/8	$\frac{1}{60}$: f/11	$\frac{1}{60}$: f/16	$\frac{1}{125}$: f/16	$\frac{1}{250}$: f/16	$\frac{1}{500}$: f/16
Whole Moon within umbra	1s: f/2	1s: f/2.8	1s; f/4	$\frac{1}{4}$: f/2.8	$\frac{1}{8}$: f/2.8	$\frac{1}{15}$: f/2.8
Mid-totality	4s: f/2	2s: f/2	2s: f/2.8	1s: f/2.8	$\frac{1}{2}$: f/2.8	$\frac{1}{4}$: f/2.8

Longer focal length lenses will often not be available in the fast focal ratios that appear above for exposures within totality. Exposures with slower focal ratios would be approximately as follows for the three films indicated:

	ISO400		ISO1000		ISO1600	
Whole Moon within umbra	2s: or f/8	1s: f/5.6	1s: or f/8	$\frac{1}{2}$: f/5.6	$\frac{1}{2}$: or f/8	$\frac{1}{4}$: f/5.6
Mid-totality	8s: or f/8	4s: f/5.6	4s: or f/8	2s: f/5.6	2s: or f/8	1s: f/5.6

With this indication of likely exposures the problem of movement by the Moon during an exposure can be considered. Assuming that a 500mm f/8 mirror lens is being used, it should yield a good image with the fastest films when the Moon is wholly within the umbra and a reasonable image during mid-totality, even though (if the exposures indicated are accurate) it will require a two-second exposure as against a target of only one second. (I am applying the formula 500/f – 'f' being 500 also in this case.) The moral for the use of even longer focal length lenses is that for best results during totality they must be mounted on a camera drive or telescope moving at the appropriate speed. Since the eclipsed Moon is a relatively indistinct object, however, it will still be worth experimenting with a fixed camera and long lenses. Incidentally, it is at a time like this that focusing by the parallax method with a bright screen (as discussed in Chapter 3) is a great advantage.

Earthshine

A much more frequent phenomenon than a lunar eclipse but one which is intriguing in its own right and a good test of improving photographic skills is the Earthshine. Sometimes called 'the Old Moon in the New Moon's arms', the ghostly glow is caused by the reflection of daylight from Earth into the night areas of the lunar surface. The cause is not fully explained in most books and is interesting.

The phase of the Moon is the opposite of that of Earth as seen from the Moon – thus, an observer on a one- or two-day waxing crescent Moon would see a waning, gibbous Earth just past full. When the waxing crescent is no more than a day or so the Earthshine effect is difficult to see because the Moon is in a relatively light sky. But as it ages to two and three days, it is still quite high as dusk falls and it faces an Earth which is still only two or three days past full. The disc of Earth looms thirteen times larger in the Moon's sky than the Moon in ours and, moreover, the Earth is four times brighter. Earthshine is the result. The effect can still be seen at four days or so but by this time Earth is waning quite appreciably as seen from the Moon and the encroaching glare from the rapidly growing daylight area of the Moon overpowers any lingering Earthshine (and stops down the iris of our eyes for good measure). The effect is reversed as the Moon wanes to a crescent. It is probable that Earthshine is brighter in winter when extensive ice and cloud cover in the northern hemisphere, and the Antarctic dur-

The Moon rising and coming out of eclipse on 30 December 1982. This is an excellent example of how well dynamic events can be portrayed on one frame of film. Using a homebuilt 4×5in sheet film camera with a 400mm f/4.5 lens, Akira Fujii made exposures at five-minute intervals. The original was shot on Ektachrome 64 film and exposures varied from $\frac{1}{2}$ a second at f/5.6 for the thin crescent to $\frac{1}{125}$ of a second at f/11 for the nearly full Moon.

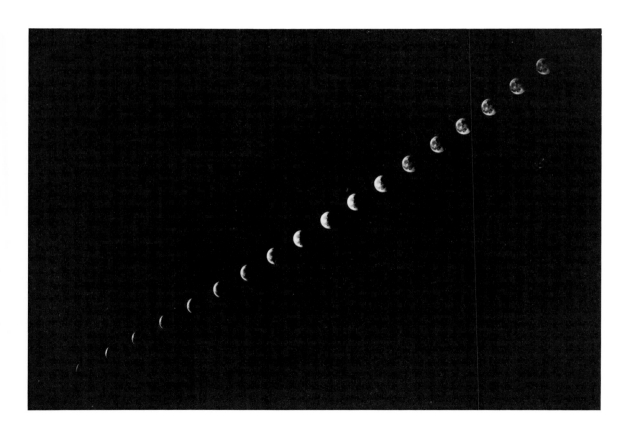

ing its summer, would reflect the highest possible light levels at the Moon.

Photographing the effect is much like photographing an eclipse. Using 500mm f/8, 1000mm f/11 and 2000mm f/11 lenses and ISO400 film, I typically bracket from the optimum $\frac{1}{60}$ or $\frac{1}{30}$ of a second for the correctly exposed crescent itself, and jump to a series of exposures of half a second, one, two, four and eight seconds. I usually find good, though naturally varying, results for the Earthshine in the one-two-four second exposure sequence. Movement of the Moon during this period must be considered but Earthshine is a very low light level and any movement is difficult to discern. The same applies to a fairly dark lunar eclipse, so those without access to a camera mount or drive should not be dissuaded from trying to photograph it. No attempt should be made to photograph Earthshine once the Moon is more than four days old: so much light comes from the crescent that the shutter speeds selected for the Earthshine result in gross overexposure of the crescent, with irradiation (or the scattering of light through the silver halide crystals of the film) causing light to spread far beyond the crescent itself.

Multi-Image Frames

Effective images and good instructional material result from a sequence of images of the Moon exposed on a single frame. The technique is very straightforward. If a special switch to override a camera's double-exposure prevention device is not available, the same effect can be secured by depressing the film rewind button in the bottom plate of the camera and then cranking the film lever wind – only this time the film will not be wound on. In a sequence of exposures of this kind, with a lapse of some minutes in between, it is imperative to remember to operate the override procedure and tension the shutter the moment an exposure has been finished, so that it becomes routine. The work of many tens of minutes can be ruined by leaving this operation until an exposure is due and then forgetting to operate the override.

We have seen that the image created on film by a 50mm lens is very small – 0.5mm maximum. However, the attraction of the 27-degree vertical and 40-degree horizontal field of view of this lens is that a large part of a lunar eclipse can be encompassed within it. When enlarged five times the overall image is by no means insignificant and – if enlarged still further with discretion – it could make a quite impressive record. Obviously settings for individual exposures have to be modified according to the stage the eclipse has reached. Longer lenses can be used but, taken with the blank spaces required, the increased diameter of the Moon on the image results in a shorter episode of the eclipse being recorded (see illustration on page 77). The same technique can be used for demonstrating simply the way in which the Moon's apparent colour changes with growing elevation from the horizon, as can be seen in the illustration on page 86.

CHAPTER SEVEN

The Sun

The beginning of this chapter is undoubtedly the most controversial part of the book. Many authors and other experienced astronomers are categorical in stating that there is only one safe way of looking at the Sun – by projecting an image through a telescope on to a white card which has been darkened compared with the surrounding daylight by some form of curtaining or by a large card through which the telescope pokes. The reason for the warning is obvious. Figures for solar energy falling on the Earth's surface include so many zeros that our minds cannot appreciate the physical facts. We can, however, appreciate the calculation that the Sun's surface is well over 250,000 times brighter than a sunlit scene on Earth; even more directly, we can appreciate the extreme discomfort (to say the least) that we experience when we glance inadvertently with the naked eye at the Sun when it comes from behind a cloud. Add to this the fact that optical instruments gather far more light and energy than the human eye – as demonstrated in party tricks such as lighting paper using a magnifying glass or lens – and the concern over photographing the Sun will be fully understood.

But these few facts are not all. The public interest in looking at the Sun is concentrated almost entirely around the time of an eclipse – especially a total eclipse. Various allegedly safe viewing filters may be proposed but many, while offering deceptively comfortable viewing of the uneclipsed portions of the solar disc, are likely to transmit infrared and ultraviolet radiation that can damage the retina *without the individual suffering pain or distress at the time of viewing*. This is because the retina, like the lens of the eye, has no pain receptors. (Although the danger of retinal burns from infrared radiation has always been stressed, research over recent years has established that there is an even greater danger from blue/UV radiation – resulting in what is called *photochemical* damage.) Smoked glass is a typical example of such an unreliable, and therefore dangerous, 'filter'. The behaviour of individuals compounds the problem and at the time of eclipses stories abound of people participating in responsibly organized viewing sessions who make such suggestions as piercing a hole in a safe filter 'to see the Sun more clearly'. To be frank, very little evidence is available about the incidence of damage to people's retinas on such occasions, but, given the apparent lack of wisdom on the part of some members of the general public, the considerable concern felt about direct viewing of the Sun must be appreciated.

The fact remains that there are perfectly safe filters for observing and photographing the Sun at modest cost to the newcomer to astrophotography. A safety drill has to be observed but it is assumed that anybody reading this book will realize the vital importance of following the correct procedure. There is no ambiguity about the filters and the procedures that are safe, but good sense must stress the value of the maxim *if in doubt, DON'T*. While the health of our eyes must take obvious precedence over possible damage to equipment, it is worth pointing out that – with reference to the use of telescopes for projecting the Sun on to white card – one of the world's biggest manufacturers of the instruments categorically advises against the practice because of the potential damage that could result from the build-up of intense heat within a telescope focused on the Sun.

Specialist filters used for viewing and photographing the Sun (see Chapter 12) reduce the level of solar radiation by a factor of 100,000 – that is, they transmit just 0.001 per cent and block 99.999 per cent. The same effect can be achieved by the newcomer to astrophotography, although two stages are involved.

Photographing any part (no matter how small) of the surface – or *photosphere* – of the Sun can be accomplished by the use of neutral-density filters with a density level of 5.0. This does not mean a 5X filter as ordinary photographers understand it – in which the 5 refers to the amount (or factor) by which the filter reduces the light and therefore by which a normal unfiltered exposure must be increased to achieve a comparable result when using the filter. A neutral-density (ND) value of 5.0 in fact represents a filter factor of 100,000 – the amount required for photographing the Sun. (For good measure it must also be pointed out that this figure should not be confused with that of an ND filter with a density level of 0.5, which has a filter factor of a mere 3X.)

Gelatine ND filters are available, but since a single gelatine filter with a density of 5.0 is not available, two must be combined – a 4.0 with a 1.0 or a 3.0 with a 2.0. This has no significant effect on image sharpness. The filters must be handled carefully, however, and a gelatine filter holder is a wise purchase to help protect the filter. (Glass ND filters are available in the UK but since their prices in diameters up to 122mm are comparable to the specialized solar filters already referred to they are unlikely to be purchased by newcomers and are not discussed further here.) The drawback with the ND filters is that they block only the visible spectrum by the

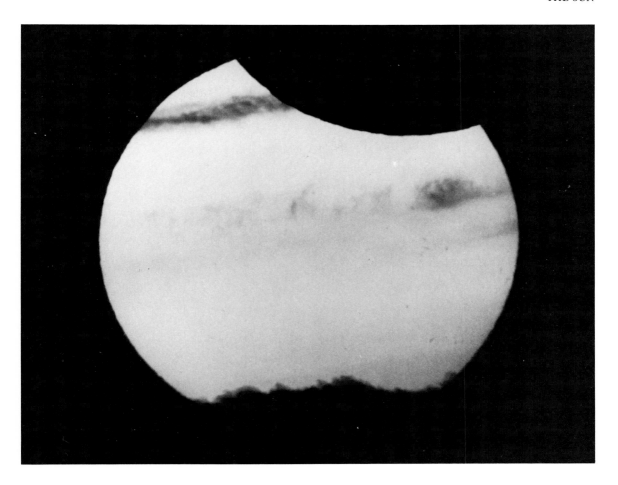

Those with a technical interest want totally clear skies for eclipse photography of the Sun. However, the presence of some cloud can result in intriguing photographs – as here. Seen from the UK, there was a partial eclipse of the Sun late in the evening of 20 July 1982. There was scattered cloud near the western horizon with quite thick stratus blanketing the bottom of the Sun and thin layers of cloud elsewhere making its disc appear almost like that of Jupiter. Small flocks of birds passing in front of the solar disc are easily seen in the original print. A sequence of colour images was exposed during the partial eclipse and this black and white copy was made from one. The originals were exposed using a 1000mm f/11 Nikkor lens and an Inconel solar filter, but a neutral density filter would have given a similar result with appropriate lenses.

81

A

B

Three images taken from a sequence of originals shot on colour film during the annular eclipse of the Sun seen from the southern USA on 30 May 1984. The first (a) was taken at 11.20am local time, the second (b) at 11.45 and the third (c) at 12.23. Sunspots are clearly visible in the first two. A complete ring (or annulus) was not seen from this location. The original pictures were taken on ISO200 colour film through a 1000mm f/11 lens with an Inconel solar filter fitted. Shutter speeds were bracketed around $\frac{1}{125}$ and $\frac{1}{60}$ of a second.

C

required amount and not the potentially dangerous infrared and ultraviolet wavelengths. So additional protection is required for observing and – more to the point – when aiming and focusing a camera.

This extra protection is provided by black and white film of the sort we use in everyday photography. When such a film is fully exposed by unrolling or extracting it from a cassette in bright light and then developed normally, instead of the variety of tones seen in a typical negative the film consists of a dense layer of metallic silver. It has been established that such a filter with an ND value of 6.0 provides good protection for the eyes – and this density can be obtained by joining two thicknesses of the exposed and developed black and white film together (with both of the emulsion, or duller, sides facing inwards) in a suitable frame of some kind. 120 size film will provide a reasonable area for comfortable and safe viewing but two pieces of similarly treated 4 × 5 in film will be even more so. One medical opinion is that the filter should be looked through for no longer than thirty seconds at a time to allow natural processes within the eye to conduct any heat away from the retina.

In practice this means that a two-stage operation is required when photographing the Sun. The camera is aimed to frame the Sun and focusing is accomplished with the home-made viewing filter held in front of the lens of a single lens reflex. Then the composite photographic ND filter is screwed into position and the viewing filter removed before exposures are made. At no time when using an SLR should the eye be applied to the viewfinder without the *viewing* filter in position. Also *only viewing filters made from black and white film are safe and effective*. Colour films, whether of the transparency or negative-positive type, are totally unsuitable because they contain very little or no silver when exposed and processed – and it is the metallic silver which protects the eyes. Polarizing filters, too, are unsuitable. Incidentally, the viewing filter itself cannot be used for photography because the metallic silver scatters light and a slightly blurred image results.

Finally, you need to remember good, basic photographic practice if you are engaged in a lengthy session photographing the Sun – as during an eclipse. The camera (and the film inside) should be kept shaded while photography is not taking place. Moreover, since the photographic ND filters do not absorb infrared wavelengths, the camera should not be pointed at the Sun continuously unless either a totally opaque card or the viewing filter is held in front of the lens. The danger to the lens and camera components from the build-up of heat is a real one.

As outlined in Chapter 1, despite the Sun's diameter being 400 times greater than that of the Moon, the two bodies have approximately the same angular diameter as seen from Earth. An eclipse of the Sun occurs when a new Moon lies precisely between it and the Earth, an event rendered considerably less frequent than seems likely by the approximately five-degree inclination to the ecliptic of the Moon's orbit about the Earth. If the Moon is at a point closest to the Earth in its orbit (perigee) at the time of the line-up, then the size of the totally shadowed area it creates on the Earth (the umbra) is at its largest possible diameter of about 270km (167 miles), and totality for observers in the optimum position can last for the maximum time ever possible of somewhat more than seven minutes. Often, the size of the umbra is less and therefore the period of totality considerably shorter. If the line-up occurs with the Moon at its farthest point from the Earth (apogee) its disc does not cover all of the Sun, the umbra does not reach the surface of the Earth, and a narrow ring of the solar photosphere outlines the Moon. This is called an annular eclipse, which tends

to attract far less interest than a total eclipse with its dramatic sights.

As Sun and Moon keep pace with each other for two hours or so during a total eclipse, a path of totality sweeps across the surface of the Earth at a speed – depending on the height of the Moon in the sky – of as much as 8000km/h (5000mph). Observers outside the line of totality but within the penumbra of the Moon's shadow see a partial eclipse only. Solar eclipses and the path of totality (if any) are predicted well in advance and one published list gives details to the year 2510! It is calculated that the average period between eclipse paths crossing the same location on the Earth's surface is 400 years.

(Below) **As soon as a solar eclipse begins, light passing through the foliage of a tree takes on the shape of the visible solar disc.**

(*Above*) When holidaying in Norway or at a
similar latitude it is worth keeping a careful watch
for the aurora borealis. This picture was obtained
aboard a coastal steamer, which accounts for the
slightly crooked star trails recorded over a five-
second exposure as the ship rolled gently. The
exposure was delayed deliberately until an aircraft
taking off from nearby appeared to be flying through
the aurora. The lens used was a 50mm f/1.4
Nikkor and the film was ISO1000 3M (Scotch).

(*Right*) The beautiful 'diamond ring' effect was
photographed by George T. Keene from Lavina,
Montana, in the USA at second contact during the
solar eclipse of 26 February 1979. Some parts of the
(pink) photosphere can still be seen. An f/7
1000mm focal length telescope was used with an
exposure of $\frac{1}{1000}$ of a second on Ektachrome ISO400
film. No filter was used.

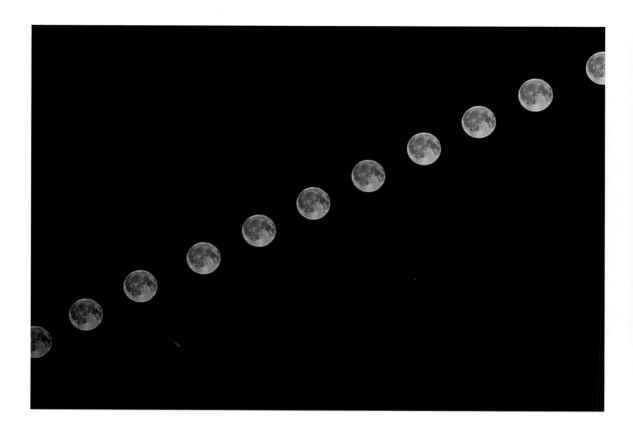

It is relatively easy to override the double-exposure prevention device on most cameras and to secure 'time lapse' images of this kind and the one that appears on page 77. That image graphically recorded the phases of a lunar eclipse; this one records the more mundane colour changes which occur when the Moon rises and shines through a narrower envelope of the atmosphere. The overall colour balance is a feature of a particular film (and another film used at the same time would record the Moon with subtle differences), but the growing brightness and lightening hue result from reduced atmospheric scattering as the Moon climbs higher. The lens used here was a 180mm f/2.8 Nikkor and

the film was ISO400 Ektachrome. The exposure was unmodified throughout at $\frac{1}{250}$ of a second. The time pause between exposures was five minutes.

Total Eclipses of the Sun to 1995

Date	Location	Maximum Duration of Totality
18 March 1988	Indian Ocean, Indonesia, Northern Pacific	3min 46sec
22 July 1990	Northern Europe, Northern Asia, Northern Pacific	2min 33sec
11 July 1991	Pacific Ocean, Hawaii, Mexico, South America	6min 54sec
30 June 1992	South Atlantic	5min 20sec
3 November 1994	Pacific Ocean, South America, South Atlantic	4min 28sec
24 October 1995	Middle & Far East, India, Malaysia, Pacific Ocean	2min 10sec

As the slender crescent of the photosphere diminishes and the shadow of totality rushes towards observers, the last remnants of sunlight shine between valleys and mountains on the Moon's leading limb as 'Baily's Beads', with the last flash of light creating an effect graphically called a 'Diamond Ring'. As this disappears, the red rim composed of the gases of the chromosphere is seen for a brief period, as are prominences – sheets of hot gas or plasma writhing for tens of thousands of kilometres into space from the Sun's surface where they become embedded in the corona, the beautiful, pearly hue that remains in view as totality progresses. As seen from Earth, a pseudo-night falls and planets (often including Venus), stars and sometimes previously undetected Sun-grazing comets, are seen clearly. But all too soon the Moon's trailing limb moves on. The first rays of sunlight are seen and the progression of Diamond Ring, Baily's Beads and crescent Sun repeat themselves in reverse order. There is a natural desire just to watch one of Nature's greatest displays, but for the photographer there is a need to concentrate on a plan.

There are two distinct phases in photographing an eclipse. During the short minutes of totality, when the photosphere is hidden in its entirety by the lunar disc, both viewing and photographic ND filters may be lowered or removed from lenses. At all other times both sets of filters *must* be used. Photographic exposures of the Sun's disc using the 5.0 value ND filter remain the same whether the Sun is 'full' or only the slenderest of crescents. The following formulae give a sound basis for calculating exposures during these phases of the Sun. (Remember that the Sun is an *extended* object.)

87

Focal ratio squared = Film speed × shutter speed × 100

or

$$\text{Shutter speed} = \frac{\text{Focal ratio squared}}{\text{Film speed} \times 100}$$

As an example in the latter case, assume that an ISO200 film and a focal ratio of f/11 has been chosen. Then:

$$\text{Shutter speed} = \frac{11 \times 11}{200 \times 100} = \frac{(121)}{(20,000)} = \frac{1}{165}$$

There is no shutter speed of this value so we can choose either $\frac{1}{125}$ or $\frac{1}{250}$ of a second, using them as the basis for bracketing the exposures.

Exposures for the various features of totality is a matter of experience, but the table gives some guidance on these exposures as well as the partial eclipse phases for those whose mathematics is a little suspect. I stress once again that exposures should be bracketed, although pre-eclipse tests of exposures using the ND filters can be carried out to get more precise exposure values for photographic coverage outside the period of totality. High-resolution black and white film is normally used in advanced studies of the Sun but only colour film can do justice to the glorious sights of totality.

Exposures are but one of the considerations facing the photographer during the eclipse. As with photography of the Moon (discussed in Chapter 6), focal length is important and the same approximate calculation (focal length/100 = diameter of the disc on the film in millimetres) needs to be made. We must consider also the subject movement threshold we have proposed, of 500/focal length. There is yet a

third, practical matter to consider. The largest size of modestly priced, gelatine ND filters readily available is 75mm square. This obviously limits the lenses of long focal length that can be used to those with a front element diameter of effectively 72mm – which means a maximum focal length of about 500mm. As we have already seen in the case of the Moon, such a lens gives an image of some 5mm diameter on the 35mm film frame which is satisfactory – and its five-degree angle of view also allows adequate space for recording the solar corona.

The table should be reviewed together with the choice of lens, so that a careful choice of film speed can be made. The best possible film quality is important, and in general this will result from the use of slow/moderate speed films. In this case, there is a penalty in the need for faster focal ratios or the use of slower shutter speeds, but the values indicated in the table are by no means too daunting.

When relatively slow shutter speeds are contemplated, precise and careful discipline is required along the lines detailed in Chapter 5. Ensure that the tripod is as firm as possible. Don't rush exposures, although there is a natural temptation to do so during totality, allow a few seconds at least to elapse between them so that vibrations induced by firing the shutter and operating the lever wind are dampened. Make sure, too, that ample film is available for the planned number of exposures during the few minutes of totality. It is better to load a new film (possibly of a faster speed) in good time for totality than to run out. Make sure it is loaded correctly and is winding on before the great moment arrives. If you do reload, the period immediately afterwards would be a good time to remove the filters and check that focusing, shutter speed and focal ratio are as required.

An alternative to taking a series of individual pictures is to expose a series of images on one frame (by overriding the double-exposure prevention device), as explained when discussing photography of the Moon in Chapter 6. A 200mm focal length lens cannot be used to cover the entire eclipse but gives an impressive solar disc – its angle of view of more than twelve degrees allows approximately ten exposures with pauses of up to five minutes between each exposure on the 35mm frame. For the most attractive result, the predicted times for the period of totality should be obtained and an attempt made to start the first exposure at a time which allows the exposure made at totality to appear in the middle of the frame. This totality exposure will be the only one exposed without the ND filters in place, and the shutter speed/focal ratio will need to be altered accordingly.

Relatively few of us are fortunate enough to see a total eclipse of the Sun, which is one of the prime reasons for joining an astronomy party going abroad. There is fascinating, more advanced photographic work to be done in studying the Sun (see Chapter 12) but in terms of emotion there is nothing to rival one's first eclipse.

Photography of the Sun:

FILM SPEED ISO	PARTIAL PHASES (5.0 ND Filter)	TOTALITY (No filters)				
		Baily's Beads	Diamond Ring	Prominences	Inner Corona	Outer Corona
25	f/5.6: $\frac{1}{125}$	f/11: $\frac{1}{125}$	f/8: $\frac{1}{60}$	f/4: $\frac{1}{125}$	f/2.8: $\frac{1}{30}$	f/2.8: $\frac{1}{4}$
64	f/8: $\frac{1}{125}$	f/11: $\frac{1}{250}$	f/8: $\frac{1}{125}$	f/5.6: $\frac{1}{125}$	f/4: $\frac{1}{30}$	f/4: $\frac{1}{4}$
125	f/11: $\frac{1}{125}$	f/11: $\frac{1}{500}$	f/8: $\frac{1}{250}$	f/8: $\frac{1}{125}$	f/5.6: $\frac{1}{30}$	f/5.6: $\frac{1}{4}$
200	f/16: $\frac{1}{125}$	f/16: $\frac{1}{500}$	f/8: $\frac{1}{500}$	f/11: $\frac{1}{125}$	f/8: $\frac{1}{30}$	f/8: $\frac{1}{4}$
400	f/16: $\frac{1}{250}$	f/16: $\frac{1}{1000}$	f/11: $\frac{1}{500}$	f/16: $\frac{1}{125}$	f/8: $\frac{1}{60}$	f/8: $\frac{1}{8}$
1000	f/16: $\frac{1}{500}$	f/22: $\frac{1}{1000}$	f/16: $\frac{1}{500}$	f/16: $\frac{1}{250}$	f/8: $\frac{1}{125}$	f/8: $\frac{1}{15}$

CHAPTER EIGHT

The Stars

The constellations are a natural subject for astrophotography. Identifying and photographing them is an enjoyable and instructive method of finding out about the sky.

The lenses used for recording the constellations are of relatively short focal lengths. The best way of finding out the most suitable focal lengths is by practice. Go out with a camera and lenses on a good, clear night and look through them at constellations which are well placed during the evening. Those that are highest will be the most suitable. Looking at a star map in advance will help not only in locating the constellations but in appreciating their relative sizes in the sky.

Many of the constellations will fit into the 27-degree (vertical) and 40-degree (horizontal) angle of view of the 50mm focal length lens. Thus in the northern winter sky it is possible to photograph Auriga or Gemini or Cassiopeia conveniently with this lens. It will also cover the whole of Orion or Perseus, but only if the camera is angled so that the long axis of the field of view accommodates the greater 'length' of the constellations compared with their 'width'. Some of the constellations are much smaller – Lyra fits comfortably into the field of view of an 85mm focal length lens – whereas others need the greater coverage (38 × 55 degrees) of a wide-angle lens. Ursa Major, Leo, Taurus and Hercules come into this latter category. (These rereferences are to the full extent of the constellations. The more readily recognized parts of Ursa Major – the Plough – and of Leo, for example, fit into the field of view of a 50mm focal length lens, but the entire constellations are far bigger.) The Summer Triangle – the beautiful multi-constellation feature embracing Vega in Lyra, Altair in Aquila and Deneb in Cygnus – also requires a wide-angle lens. Some constellations are even bigger and demand a full 24mm wide-angle lens. Hydra – the largest constellation in the sky – falls into this category.

For those who like a little mathematics, another way of working out this information is to establish the size that a given astronomical object will occupy on a 35mm film frame. This can be worked out with the formula:

$$s = \frac{a \times f}{57.3}$$

where a is the size of the object in degrees of arc, f is the focal length of the lens and s is the size of the image (in the same units as the focal length). As an example, the distance from Dubhe to Alkaid at extreme ends of the Plough is 26 degrees, so if we use a 50mm lens the size of the image is:

$$\frac{26 \times 50}{57.3} = \text{almost } 23\text{mm}$$

This will fit comfortably into the nominal 23 × 34mm picture size of a mounted 35mm slide.

This introduction points the way, but the individual photographer should gain personal, practical experience of 'fitting' different focal lengths to various constellations. If the ultimate purpose is to prepare a set of constellation slides for teaching, you will need to give some thought in due course to the choice of a single focal length so that the size of the field of view does not alter between slides – which would confuse students. Similarly, a standard might be established whereby the celestial equator always appears along the long axis of the picture frame. The 35mm wide-angle lens is in many ways suitable, but for the larger constellations you will need to select a 28mm or 24mm focal length lens – despite drawbacks in other directions which will be discussed later.

Star Trails

Having begun to find your way among the stars and before I start to go into too much detail on theory and technicalities, I suggest that you find a sky as far as possible away from city lights, load the camera with a moderate speed colour film (ISO200 or 400, no faster), set a 50mm lens at f/2.8 (no faster, even if it does open up to f/1.8 or more), select a number of constellations and shoot ten-minute time exposures of each. If the sky is reasonably dark (and using as an example a viewpoint in the northern hemisphere), make one exposure, lasting for about thirty minutes, of the Ursa Minor region, with Polaris centred in the frame. Then, turn the camera to the south and, checking with the star atlas for constellations through which the celestial equator runs, photograph that region too for thirty minutes.

When the film has been processed, the ten-minute exposures will not only record the stars as trails – thereby demonstrating the fifteen degrees per hour rotation of the Earth during the exposure – but the trails will vary considerably in colour. When exposures are made aimed at recording the stars as points of light they are often long enough for the brighter stars to overexpose and therefore appear generally whitish in colour. With photographs of trails, the light from the individual stars slowly moves across the film, so that the degree of exposure on film is much less, and more colour is present. However, the whites, light blues, yellows, oranges and reds

A wide angle lens is best suited for demonstrating clearly the apparent paths of stars on either side of the celestial equator – which runs from lower left to upper right through Orion's belt at the centre of this picture. The very bright trail at the bottom is that of Sirius. If the star trails at top and bottom are compared it is readily apparent that they arch in opposite directions – that is, around the respective celestial poles. A 24mm f/2.8 Nikkor lens was used for this picture and the original fifteen minutes' exposure was on Agfachrome 1000RS Professional film.

in the picture are not scientifically accurate records of the colours of the stars, since a number of variables are involved, such as how well the balance between the different colour-sensitive layers in the film is maintained.

Nonetheless, the colours are usually a good approximation and the film has a greater ability to distinguish (and record) the hues than our dark-adapted eyes possess. So we see white Castor compared with yellow Pollux in Gemini; the massive, orange-red Betelgeuse in Orion compared with the brilliant white

Rigel (which is 60,000 times more luminous than our Sun); the blueness of Vega in Lyra compared with the light orange of Arcturus in Bootes. In this way the straightforward exposures graphically reveal different surface temperatures of the stars, and we can divide them into different spectral types – from the very hot O-type stars down through B (hot-white, like Rigel), A (cooler white, such as Sirius – the brightest star in the night sky), through F and G (yellow, like our Sun), to K (orange, like Arcturus) and M (orange-red, like Betelgeuse). The mnemonic for remembering the types is the rather delightful Oh, Be A Fine Girl and Kiss Me.

The picture centred on Polaris (see page 49) will also show different colours but the greatest interest is in the demonstration of how Polaris lies very close to the celestial north pole – it scarcely has a trail in photographs taken with a wide-angle or normal lens. It will also reveal how the trails left by the stars around it increase in length (despite all having been recorded for the same amount of time) the farther they are away – i.e. as their declination decreases they appear to travel farther (or move faster, to put it another way). This intriguing demonstration of celestial geometry is matched by that in the picture of the equator (opposite). Here the stars on the actual equator appear to be travelling in straight lines and for the greatest distance, whereas those to the north record an increasingly curved (but shorter) trail the farther they are away from the equator. The stars to the south behave similarly although the curve is in the opposite direction – that of the south celestial pole. Both pictures, despite being quite simple to obtain, are extremely useful in suggesting, within the inevitable limits of a flat surface, the three-dimensional nature of the celestial sphere above our heads.

As with many other pictures the addition of pictorial elements in the foreground can heighten impact – a mountain or castle beneath Polaris or a constellation angled close to the horizon and reflected in water. But the main reason for suggesting that you start with the simplest exercises in star photography is that, notwithstanding the simplicity, sound knowledge is derived from the results.

The Stars as 'Points of Light'

Since the approach of this book is to consider astrophotography using essentially photographic equipment, the major question is how to overcome the effects of the rotation of the Earth within this limitation.

In Chapter 2 I referred to the focal length of lenses and to the fact that the stars – which may be described as point sources to distinguish them from extended objects – were so far away that the image size on the film was not related to focal length. While one may talk loosely about their images on film as being points of light, this is not in fact accurate. The magnitude of a star, lens and film characteristics, length of exposure and the atmosphere all affect the end result so that a bright star such as Vega, for example, will be recorded clearly on film as a much bigger 'point of light' than stars of lower magnitude (see illustration overleaf). The concept of the image size of a star on film is important because, if an exposure is short enough to record the star at a critical threshold value which does not show movement resulting from the Earth's rotation, then the ability to take more realistic pictures than those showing star trails is within reach.

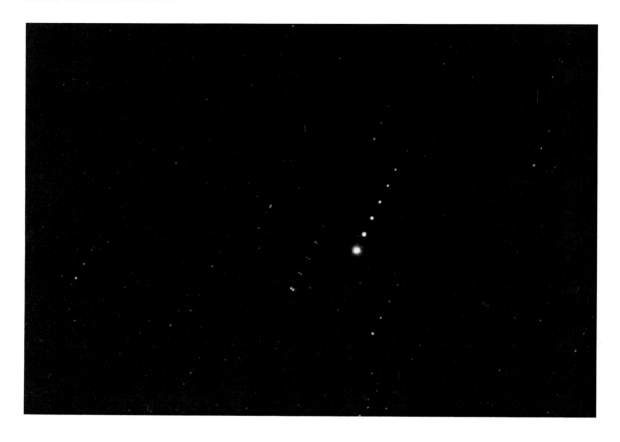

(Above) When is a point source not a point of light? The answer should perhaps be 'always'. Lens characteristics (for example shooting at different f-numbers) as well as over or underexposure can affect the apparent size of a star on film. Here the brilliant star Vega was photographed (although some nearby companions were also recorded) using the Noct-Nikkor 58mm f/1.2 lens, – which is specially designed for night photography. However, the governing factor here is gross exposure. The lens was first opened to its widest aperture at f/1.2 and a four-second exposure given. Two minutes were allowed for Vega to move far enough for the next image to be exposed on a different part of the film and then a four-second exposure was given with the aperture at f/2 – and so on down to f/8. The film used was ISO400 black and white. This experiment demonstrates how bright stars become overexposed (and tend to lose colour) in time exposures calculated to record fainter stars.

(*Above*) Copying pictures tends to build up contrast and this can be very useful for finding features which are not clear or virtually invisible in some originals. This is a copy made from a colour transparency on high speed film (exposed for six minutes using a camera drive) which shows the Sagittarius region of the Milky Way (compare with the colour illustration on page 50). Saturn is the bright point of light not far from the right edge of the picture. It is the bright star clouds of the Milky Way which first attract the eye but in a contrasty picture they also serve to accentuate the so-called dark nebulae which are clouds of dust in interstellar space which block the starlight behind from reaching us. One of the best examples of such a dark nebula is the shape seen east of Saturn and above the data block in this picture. It is sometimes called 'The Great Galactic Dark Horse' for reasons which are evident. If you have trouble seeing it, the legs extend toward the right side of the picture and the head towards the top right hand corner.

Barry Gordon, the American lecturer and writer on astrophotography, has devised such a value based on a combination of experience and calculation. He selected 0.05mm as a trail length which is short enough to be indistinguishable from the image of a point in the film. Working from that he calculated that for the fastest moving stars (i.e. those at the celestial equator) any exposure in seconds shorter than 700/f – where f is the focal length of the lens in use – will yield essentially trail-free images. (For the hypercritical, 500/f yields a trail length of 0.036mm, which is nearing the limits of a film's resolution.) The value for stars away from the equator (which, as our trail pictures have shown, appear to move more slowly) is even more in the photographer's favour and for stars at declination 50 degrees the exposure can be set at 1000/f. This means, therefore, that if we are using a 50mm standard focal length lens an exposure may last for 700/50 = 14 seconds without showing trailing. Of course, all the other factors involved must be such to allow an exposure of this duration.

These factors include film speed, film latitude, lens speed, star magnitudes, and the condition of the atmosphere (which can drastically attenuate the light from stars) as major elements. Remember, too, that when photographing point sources it is the absolute diameter of the lens which is important, not the focal ratio. The former is calculated quite easily by dividing the focal length of a lens by its focal ratio – thus, a 50mm f/1.8 lens has a diameter of just under 28mm. Because so many variables are involved guidance on exposures cannot be precise, but the following table gives suggestions for stars to just beyond naked-eye visibility (approximately magnitude 6) when some typical lenses are used at maximum diameter or aperture – i.e. not 'stopped down' at all:

Lens	Diameter (mm)	Film (ISO Speed)			
		200 (exposure)	400	1000	1600
24mm f/2.8	8.6	15m	8m	4m	2m
35mm f/1.4	25	2m	1m	30s	15s
50mm f/1.8	28	2m	1m	30s	15s
85mm f/2.8	30	2m	1m	30s	15s
180mm f/2.8	64	30s	15s	8s	4s

The demands made by camera design – for example, the need to reduce vignetting to a minimum and for the back of the lens not to foul the reflex mirror – result in photographic lenses being constructed in such a way that the effective diameter of many is not quite as simple to calculate as suggested above. The front diameter in such cases is in fact larger than the f-number would suggest. The calculations become a little complicated but nonetheless the information given in the table may still be regarded with confidence as a basis for experimentation. The wide-angle 24mm focal length lens is regarded by the everyday photographer as quite fast, but its diameter is so small compared with the other lenses that relatively lengthy time exposures are required when it is used to photograph the stars.

Stopping down a lens inevitably reduces the effective diameter – thus if the lenses in the table are stopped down to their next focal ratio value, the diameter too is reduced to the extent that time exposures using ISO1000 film have to be increased to those appearing in the ISO400 film column.

We may now revert to the formula for trail-free star images. Using the 50mm focal length lens gives us a 'safe' exposure time of around fourteen seconds if we assume that we are photographing stars on the celestial equator, but about twenty seconds if our subjects are around 50 degrees declination – such as Ursa Major, Perseus, Andromeda, Cygnus and Auriga. The figures for the 35mm wide-angle lens are better at twenty seconds and almost thirty seconds. The 180mm focal length lens in these two cases yields trail-free time exposures of only about four and six seconds but because it has a much bigger diameter it

is by no means at a disadvantage. Correlating these figures with those in the table indicates that when using high-speed films of ISO1000 and above in a fixed camera with fast standard lenses we are able to secure photographs of stars down to magnitude 6 which are essentially free of trailing.

Of course, if we curb our ambitions and aim to record stars down to magnitude 3 only, for example, then the exposure times are shortened considerably. Using ISO1000 film and the 50mm f/1.8 or the 35mm f/1.4 lens at maximum aperture requires exposure times as short as four seconds – while even the 24mm f/2.8 lens yields a more manageable exposure of thirty seconds.

The above guidance should be used only as a starting point for experimentation and to establish the quality of the results available in inevitably greatly varying circumstances (from equipment to the nature of the night sky).

In general, slower films yield higher quality than faster ones, but the advances in film technology have not only created a revolution in film speeds but also secured levels of quality quite unheard of just a few years ago. These improvements have affected black and white as well as both types of colour film (transparency and negative). It is these changes that have given the newcomer to astrophotography the chance to photograph the constellations with what is, in effect, non-astronomical equipment. (It is a revelation for somebody who has been taking astrophotographs for some years to see the way in which exposures of a matter of seconds in optimum circumstances can begin to record diffuse nebulae – objects which hitherto have taken exposures of many minutes' duration.)

A

In taking photographs using camera drives and telescopes we normally record star magnitudes much fainter than those visible to the human eye. This can at first be confusing for the relative newcomer to astrophotography when trying to interpret the photographs. Photograph (a), taken from a high speed colour original exposed for six minutes using a 24mm f/2.8 Nikkor lens mounted on a camera drive, is of the northern Milky Way in the region of the 'Summer Triangle' which is comprised of Vega in Lyra, Deneb in Cygnus and Altair in Aquila. South is at top. The picture is rich in detail but some may find it a little difficult to distinguish Deneb, just to the left of the data block, Vega which is the bright star further to the left and Altair which is top centre.

Compare this picture with (b), which results from a 30 second exposure on fast black and white film in a fixed camera using the same wide angle lens. The detail is much less but the Summer Triangle is immediately apparent – as is the 'northern cross' of Cygnus. This comparison suggests that pictures intended to assist constellation recognition should not be exposed for lengthy periods.

B

It is all extremely encouraging and it is almost certain that the exposure values given above understate the potential, since one film may have more latitude – or better reciprocity characteristics – than another, and can therefore record stars that are fainter than the target of magnitude 6. Hence part of your test programme should include comparing the different films of allegedly similar speed.

Despite this encouraging situation, we should be aware that we are pushing at the limits – that we are, in effect, 'snatching' pictures to combat the rotation of the Earth. To do this we are using fast lenses wide open (here focal ratio and diameter are as one), and we are paying the penalties: off-axis coma and other aberrations present problems, and it is an unpalatable truth that wide-angle lenses, in particular, perform best at about three stops slower than the maximum. Although not strictly an aberration, vignetting is also likely to take place. We can compensate for these to some degree by keeping important objects away from the edges of the field of view whenever possible – but how can that be done with a large constellation which is filling the frame? In some circumstances we may just have to grin and bear it.

Nor do the problems stem from within the camera and lens alone. The very fast focal ratio of our lenses, combined with fast films, records extended objects quickly – and there are two such 'objects' which can intrude strongly into our pictures: the night sky itself, and light pollution. The former may seem a little surprising, but the airglow – photochemical emissions from atoms and molecules in the upper atmosphere – can be recorded in relatively long exposures. If the sky in such exposures appears to be pale green, it could be because this is the wavelength emitted by atomic oxygen. No difficulty should be encountered during exposures lasting up to a few minutes but airglow could certainly be recorded in the exposures of from ten to thirty minutes that were suggested earlier for star-trail photographs. This is why I suggested that the focal ratio used should be held to f/2.8 and no faster. Although not perhaps so exotic, moonlight has an obvious and even more powerful ability to render the fainter stars invisible. (In a long-exposure photograph taken when a full or near-full Moon is up, the sky appears almost as blue as it does during the day.) A crescent Moon is bearable but, as the phase grows, the deep-space astrophotographer has to forget photography for a while and be occupied instead with jobs such as checking equipment and preparing for future tasks.

Light pollution is a serious problem. In and around large urban areas its effects are obvious. The sky is not black, or even dark at all, and only the brightest stars may be seen beyond the pall of orange light (if sodium street lights predominate) that covers the sky and which deepens the closer our eyes or cameras look towards the horizon. In areas lit by mercury street lights, blue predominates in place of orange. The effect when taking photographs with fast focal ratios is that the colour film rapidly records the predominant colour of the light pollution and many of the less bright stars are lost to view.

Assuming that it is impossible to get away from light pollution, its impact can be limited by reducing the focal ratio. But this also reduces the effective diameter of the lens, so that while the pollution may be curtailed the fainter stars will also be lost. A more sophisticated possibility is to switch to a lens with the same diameter (and therefore star-gathering power) but a longer focal length, which means a slower focal ratio. The problem then will be whether the longer focal length (taken with the other factors) will permit an exposure short enough to avoid trailing of star images.

While the intention is not to exaggerate the limitations imposed by light-polluted skies it is something of which the newcomer should be fully aware. Creative use of the lens may help but, in the end, the only effective solution may be to travel to a location with darker skies, or to 'grin and bear it'.

An Equatorial Mount

A means of breaking away from the restraints imposed by the rotation of the Earth is to fix the camera on a mount that is aligned accurately on the celestial pole and moves through right ascension. The camera lens can thus track the stars so that relative to the camera they appear stationary. This is the system used on many telescopes and also spe-

A

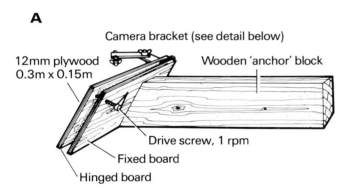

Camera bracket (see detail below)

12mm plywood 0.3m x 0.15m

Wooden 'anchor' block

Drive screw, 1 rpm

Fixed board

Hinged board

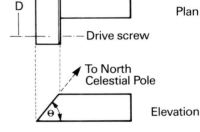

Hinge line

D

Plan

Drive screw

To North Celestial Pole

θ

Elevation

Wood or metal strip

¼" Whitworth machine screws

Camera

Wing nuts

Shelf bracket

Door hinge

Critical dimensions:

θ = observer's latitude.

D depends on drive screw specification, as follows:

6mm SI
0 BA } (1 thread/mm) D = 229mm

¼" Whitworth (20 threads/in) D = 291mm

B

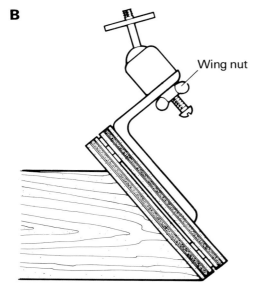

Wing nut

C

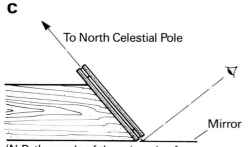

To North Celestial Pole

Mirror

(N.B. the angle of the mirror is of no consequence
– it need not be horizontal)

(Previous page) **How to make a Haig equatorial camera mount. (a)**

(Top) **The Haig mount, using a ball and socket head. (b)**

(Above) **Polar alignment of the Haig mount by sighting along a hinge line, using a mirror. (c)**

cially designed camera mounts – most of which are powered by electric motors. While these mounts are briefly described in Chapter 14, they are more suitable for advanced astrophotography than for beginners. However, good results and valuable experience may be gained from a manual mount which can be built without too much difficulty. This was designed some years ago by Mr George Haig of Renfrewshire in Scotland, and is known as the Haig mount or the Scotch mount. A description of how to build and operate the mount is shown here.

The implications of the use of this or any equatorial mount will be evident immediately. Longer time exposures can be given, and film and lens settings selected for optimum effect (such as limiting aberrations), rather than just to avoid star trailing, as when a fixed camera is used.

The Haig (Scotch) Equatorial Camera Mount

The main base or 'anchor' of George Haig's manual equatorial drive is a block of wood

(Opposite) **On the evening of 29 November 1984, Venus and Jupiter joined the crescent Moon (bottom right) while Mars was high to the east (towards the top left) in the constellation Capricornus. The original colour photograph (on 3M – Scotch – ISO1000 film) showed how much better fast film can distinguish colours in a darkening sky than can the human eye. The exposure was for four seconds and the lens a 50mm f/1.4 Nikkor. Usually street and other lights are to be avoided but on this occasion they and the reflections on the waters of Langstone Harbour added some appeal to the composition.**

(*Left*) When the Moon rose on 4 May 1985 over the UK, totality of a lunar eclipse was just beginning. The eastern horizon from southern Hampshire was not clear and the Moon was not seen until after totality ended at 20.30UT. This picture was taken at 21.07, about twenty-nine minutes before the Moon moved completely out of the umbra. The exposure was calculated for the penumbra area and was $\frac{1}{8}$ of a second on ISO200 Ektachrome film using the 1000mm Nikkor f/11 mirror-reflex. A shorter exposure would have been expected, but the sky was still hazy even as the Moon was climbing well away from the horizon.

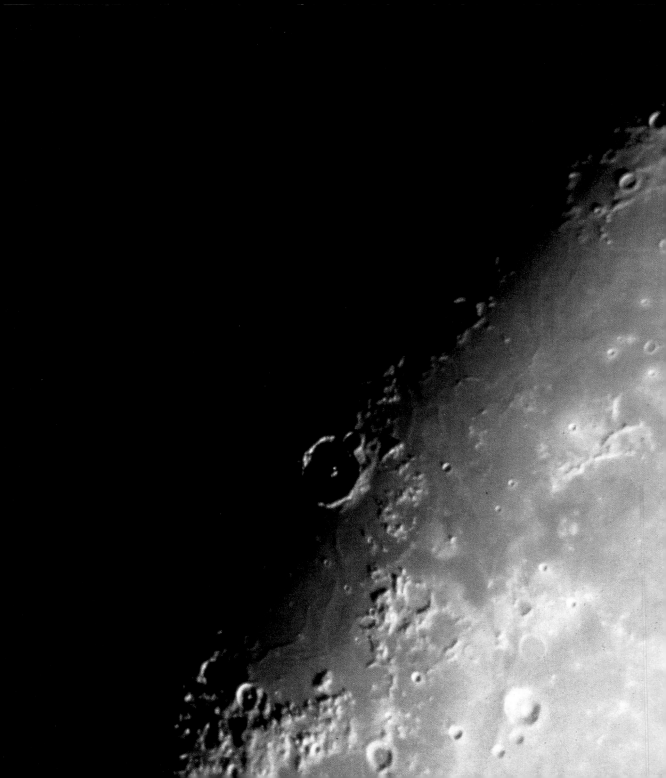

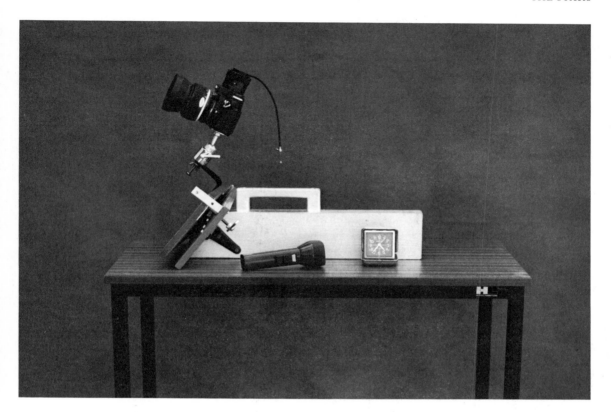

(*Opposite*) **Eyepiece projection using a 25mm ocular yielding an effective focal length of more than 12,000mm with the Celestron Super C8 telescope secured this image of the lunar surface. The terminator, or line between day and night, runs through the Mare Humorum in the lower part of the picture, and the crater prominently etched by sunlight is Gassendi. The two much smaller but clearly seen craters at the top are Kepler and Encke. Edges of lava flows are easily distinguished in the floors of the maria. The original photograph was exposed on ISO200 Ektachrome Professional film for two seconds at f/60.**

(*Above*) **The Haig manual guider on a firm base with clock and red-light torch. The hinges are on the other side of the guider out of view, but clearly seen is the rotating bolt which at one revolution per minute opens the boards, thus enabling the camera to track the stars.**

A four-minute exposure of the Taurus area using the Haig manual guider. The guider enabled the 35mm wide-angle Nikkor lens to be stopped down from f/1.4 to f/2.8 for better control of off-axis aberrations. The film was Tri-X rated at ISO400 and developed in HC110 (dilution B). Plainly seen, right of centre, are the Pleiades with the 'V-shaped' Hyades and Aldebaran below to the left. The top of Orion (with Betelgeuse prominent) is on the lower left, Auriga towards the top left with part of Perseus above the Pleiades.

about 30cm (1ft) or so long with a cross-section of some 7 × 10cm (3 × 4in). One end is sawn carefully at an angle equal to that of the latitude where it will be used. A piece of board at least 15 × 30cm (6 × 12in) in area and up to 15mm ($\frac{3}{5}$in thick) is carefully fixed to the sawn end by glue and/or wood screws as shown. Another board of the same dimensions is attached to it by means of two hinges which are fitted very accurately in line with one other.

A bolt or drive screw is inserted through the fixed board at a distance from the hinges,

which is calculated on the basis of one complete revolution of the screw moving the board by the correct angular rate to track the stars. This depends in turn on the pitch of the screw, and several examples are given in the diagram. A tapped bearing may be inserted in the wood for the bolt but it is quite adequate to make a slightly undersized hole in the fixed board, to work the bolt through once or twice and then to lubricate the hole with grease before threading the bolt in again and leaving it in position. A slender strip of metal or thin ply is attached to the head of the bolt so that it may be turned by one finger without creating vibration in the mount.

The camera bracket can be home-made as in diagram (a), or a shop-bought photographic ball-and-socket head as in diagram (b), and is fixed to the other hinge board as close to the hinges as possible to achieve maximum rigidity. A retaining bracket, which prevents the hinge boards from flapping open when the mount is being carried, and a carrying handle, are some of the optional extras fitted to the mount shown in the illustration on page 105, which was made by Mr Haig.

It is important that no attempt be made to fit the mount to a tripod since it could not possibly be fixed firmly enough. Instead it is recommended that the mount be placed on a level and wide wall top, steady table or some similar surface which gives convenient access for rotating the handle in time with the second hand of a watch or clock. Polar alignment along the hinge line is carried out by using a small mirror as shown in diagram (c).

I found the most convenient operating arrangement to be that shown in the photograph, seating myself to one side of the table with a small clock clearly in view. After preparing the camera, the shutter was locked open by cable release while the lens was covered with a black card. The clock was already running (illuminated by a discreetly angled red-light torch) and at a suitable moment, coinciding with a 15, 30, 45 or 60 sweep of the second hand, the card was removed and rotation of the bolt begun. I conducted tests with lenses up to only 50mm in focal length, but found it entirely satisfactory to move the drive screw at fifteen-second intervals, although after a while it was quite easy to keep pace with the second hand of the clock in a continuous movement.

Doubtless, handymen will think of ways to power the mount by a small electric motor capable of rotating the bolt at one rpm.

CHAPTER NINE

The Planets

Over the last twenty years or so interplanetary spacecraft – such as NASA's Pioneers, Mariners, Vikings and Voyagers – have sent back to Earth many thousands of pictures which have not only been of great scientific value but are often beautiful and awe-inspiring. We have been privileged to see, as though we were there, the deserts and volcanoes of Mars, the multi-coloured belts and zones of Jupiter's atmosphere and the exquisite rings of Saturn. Such pictures may lead newcomers to astrophotography to have high expectations of what may be achieved. I will state immediately that planetary photography is one of the most difficult tasks faced by even the highly experienced astro-photographer. However, this does not mean that all is lost for the novice: excellent pictures can be taken but we have to accept the

High-magnification photography of the planets is a demanding task. This image of Jupiter was obtained using eyepiece projection (with a 10mm ocular) on the Celestron telescope—the effective focal length being well over 30,000mm. The original was shot on the new Kodachrome 200 35mm colour film and the exposure was two seconds.

limitations resulting from the nature of the planets and of our equipment.

Since they are members of the solar system the planets are on the Earth's doorstep compared with the stars – but they are still relatively small. They vary in their apparent sizes depending on how far they are from us in their individual orbits at any one time. These are the figures:

Mercury   5–13 arc seconds

Venus   10–65 arc seconds

Mars   13–25 arc seconds

Jupiter   31–50 arc seconds

Saturn   15–31 arc seconds (disc)

           35–49 arc seconds (rings)

Uranus   3.4–4.2 arc seconds

Neptune   2.2–2.4 arc seconds

(If Uranus and Neptune are extremely difficult for our purposes, Pluto and the asteroids may be completely dismissed!)

At its best, the Earth's nearest planetary neighbour, Venus, is about one-thirtieth the size of the Moon when full. It is possible to work out its size on a 35mm film frame by modifying the formula used in the previous chapter:

$$s = \frac{a \times f}{206280}$$

where s is image size, f the focal length of the lens in millimetres and a is the angular size of the object in arc seconds. Working out the simple mathematics for Venus's maximum size using a powerful lens of 1000mm yields

an image of 0.32mm. This is certainly bigger than the smallest point sources our lenses and films can resolve and record but is not very exciting, to say the least.

Since Venus at the optimum time is the largest of the planets as seen from Earth, we are faced squarely with the problem of focal length. If 0.1mm is taken as the image size which is the threshold between the objects that act as point sources on one side and extended objects on the other, then the focal length required to secure it varies from about 500mm in the cases of Venus and Jupiter to around 10,000mm for Neptune. But 0.1mm is still very insignificant (a full stop in a small typeface, perhaps), and to reach image sizes where – all things being equal – some detail can be discerned demands a focal length of around 10,000mm for Venus and Jupiter and about twice that for Mars and Saturn – without considering tiny Mercury on the one extreme and distant Uranus and Neptune on the other.

Such focal lengths are clearly beyond the newcomer to astrophotography, but fortunately there is much that can be done none the less. The magnitudes of the planets vary according to their size and distance from us but, if we strike an average, all the way out to Saturn they are even at their very worst on a par with the brighter stars (down to magnitude 1.4 for Saturn when it is at its most distant).

The following table gives exposures that can be used as the basis for experimentation, using two lenses of moderate focal length but quite wide diameters (remember again that, since the planets are point sources at these focal lengths, lens speed depends on absolute diameter and not on focal ratio):

Planet	ISO400 Film (Time in seconds)	
	180mm f/2.8 (64mm diameter)	50mm f/1.8 (48mm diameter)
Mercury	$\frac{1}{15}$	$\frac{1}{8}$
Venus	$\frac{1}{250}$	$\frac{1}{125}$
Mars	$\frac{1}{8}$	$\frac{1}{4}$
Jupiter	$\frac{1}{60}$	$\frac{1}{30}$
Saturn	$\frac{1}{8}$	$\frac{1}{4}$
Uranus	15	30
Neptune	120 (2min)	240 (4min)

(While Uranus is marginally within the scope of a fixed camera, Neptune certainly requires a driven camera. Both are omitted from consideration for the rest of this chapter.)

Although most of these exposures fall within the category of what earlier were termed the 'no man's land' shutter speeds that test our technique to the full, they are none the less well within the bounds of possibility. The planets may appear to be small, but out to Saturn at least they are quite bright. This has the additional bonus, of course, of causing few worries when we apply the severe 500/ focal length test for image trailing. While separated by many tens and even hundreds of millions of kilometres, the planets frequently appear close to one another in the sky. These *conjunctions* are line-of-sight effects which present various types of picture opportunities.

In the first instance, the photographer can secure images of planets in the same field of view without too much regard for other objects – such as stars. Although a compromise exposure or bracketing will be required if, say, Mars and Jupiter are included together in the field of view (as will be evident from the table on the left), the relative brightness of the two is close enough not to result in severe over- or underexposure at any reasonable setting. Having verified your competence to secure such a picture, however, there is little lasting interest in recording two points of light on the film.

A much more interesting test is that of photographing Jupiter with one or more of its four major moons – Callisto, Ganymede, Europa and Io. Ganymede is the largest and has an apparent diameter of 1.5 arc seconds, so trying to photograph it and the other moons (assuming that they are not occluded by the planet) is a major test of lens resolution and the capability of the photographer and the equipment. The moons have magnitudes of between 4.6 and 5.6 compared with Jupiter's average −2, so that in securing images of any of the moons Jupiter is bound to be overexposed to some degree. Using a 1000mm f/11 mirror lens and ISO400 film, the moons require an exposure of approximately 2 seconds (where some small trailing may be expected) whereas Jupiter itself requires only about $\frac{1}{125}$ of a second. A sequence of exposures between the two is indicated and the illustration opposite shows one example of what can be obtained.

Jupiter and its moons can be photographed with photographic lenses, but the main problem is the different exposures needed to record Jupiter accurately on the one hand, and the moons on the other. This is a section from an original colour image obtained on Agfachrome 1000RS Professional film during a one-second exposure using an f/11 1000mm Nikkor mirror reflex. In the attempt to record some of the Galilean satellites— two of which are shown—both Jupiter and Mars (at the top) were overexposed.

It is well within the capability of photographic lenses (more especially the longer focal lengths) to record occultations by the Moon of planets and stars. Although the Moon appears to move westwards with the stars and planets as night progresses, it is actually moving eastwards in relation to the background at a speed of about 1km/s (0.621 miles per second) or across a space equal to its own diameter per hour. Inevitably, therefore, it passes in front of other bodies – events which are awaited with some eagerness by enthusiasts since careful timings of the beginning and ending of the occultation can provide valuable additional information about the positions of stars as well as the Moon's position in its orbit. The event can be dramatic too: if the Moon is waxing, the dark lunar limb first reaches the star well before the daylit portion and causes it to disappear quite suddenly (demonstrating, incidentally, that the Moon has no appreciable atmosphere, since if it had the object would fade more gradually). If the Moon is waning, the reverse happens and an occulted star will suddenly appear when the Moon's dark lunar limb passes beyond it. The disappearance of planets tends not to be so sudden, mainly because of their larger angular size compared with the stars, but also partly because they too are travelling with the Moon in an easterly direction, although not as quickly as seen from Earth.

The longer lenses are obviously preferable in recording such an event. Although the Moon is an extended object and the planets at the focal lengths used become a mixture of extended objects and point sources, the differences are manageable. The table overleaf gives target exposures for four planets:

Planet	Film ISO400	
	500mm f/8 (62mm)	1000/f11 (90mm)
Venus*	$\frac{1}{2000}$	$\frac{1}{1000}$
Mars	$\frac{1}{8}$	$\frac{1}{15}$
Jupiter*	$\frac{1}{250}$	$\frac{1}{125}$
Saturn	$\frac{1}{8}$	$\frac{1}{15}$

*These are treated as extended objects

Using ISO400 film, a typical exposure for a crescent Moon could well be $\frac{1}{60}$ of a second at f/11 and that for a full Moon $\frac{1}{250}$ or $\frac{1}{500}$ of a second at the same aperture. This clearly demonstrates that for the most part occlusions taking place during a waxing or waning crescent phase of the Moon present fewer exposure-balancing problems with Mars and Saturn, whereas Venus and Jupiter, when treated as extended objects, are perfectly compatible with the full Moon.

This all seems a little involved, so it is understandable that for many newcomers the most attractive pictures of conjunctions of the planets are relatively the easiest and least demanding in terms of equipment. These are unashamedly pictorial compositions taken at dusk or dawn, with the elements (besides the planets) including to great advantage a very slender crescent Moon and an attractive foreground. This might contain trees or buildings (there is no reason why any of these should not be lit provided the light source is low-level), or water, which provides fascinating reflections. I suggest that the photography takes place at dusk or dawn partly because there may be a chance of capturing Mercury, the elusive planet closest to the Sun, but mainly because (although the human eye is

not sensitive enough to see them) a relatively long photographic exposure can record delightful hues in the sky which are totally missing from the somewhat sterner exercises concentrating on the Jovian moons or occlusions described above.

The lens could be the normal 50mm, although I have found a 35–105mm f/3.5 zoom very useful since it gives a flexibility that is well worth the slight disadvantage of speed loss. The first table in this chapter gives target exposures for a 50mm f/1.8 lens loaded with an ISO400 film – which is again recommended because the grain structure of ISO1000 and faster films becomes extremely intrusive in the lighter skies of dusk and dawn. Since the lens will be used wide open for the planets, even though the values quoted here for the Moon have been f/8 and f/11, there is certain to be some overexposure of the Moon. However, this need not be a problem with the slender crescent phase. You will need to attempt a wide bracketing, with the longer exposures aimed at securing an attractive sky. I usually employ shutter speeds in the range $\frac{1}{60}$, $\frac{1}{30}$, $\frac{1}{15}$, $\frac{1}{4}$, $\frac{1}{2}$, 1, 2, 4 and 8 seconds, with the fastest possible aperture.

Although the planets vary a great deal in their brilliance (and none more so than Mars, from magnitude −2.3 to 1.5) bracketing is a rough and ready means of obtaining some satisfactory photographs. Having omitted Uranus and Neptune from most of our discussion, I must admit that Mercury is the most difficult subject among the remaining planets. Not only is it very small (about one third bigger in absolute diameter than the Moon, although much farther away), but it orbits so close to the Sun that it is never seen in a dark sky in temperate latitudes, and is always rela-

tively close to the horizon with the attendant problems of atmospheric haze and pollutants. Mars, because of its relatively small size and all too frequent great distance from Earth, can be difficult although it relents from time to time. Venus – the traditional evening or morning star – is by far the most brilliant of the planets, so much so that it creates something of an exposure problem when photographed with its less well-endowed companions of the ecliptic.

Venus, a waning crescent Moon and Earthshine recorded as dawn was breaking, on 25 April 1987. The original was shot on Agfachrome 1000RS Professional film—although a slower film could have been used to advantage. The lens was a 180mm f/2.8 Nikkor and the exposure was two seconds. As seen from some parts of the world, the Moon occluded Venus on this morning.

The full Moon and Venus can be photographed in the same frame without difficulty but the former should be rigorously excluded from pictorial images that include all the other planets. Trying to accommodate their lower brightness by greater exposure will result in gross overexposure of the Moon and the likely creation of its ghost image. This is a form of lens flare caused by double reflection of the bright light source between the internal surfaces of the front and back components of the lens. Most lenses suffer from the problem to some degree if a brilliant light source is included in the field of view, the ghost usually being inverted and in the opposite side of the picture to the original. The ghost image can only be exorcized by effectively diminishing its brightness by stopping the lens down – or removing it from the field of view entirely.

The final requirement for the newcomer to planetary photography is information about conjunctions, phases of the Moon and the occurrence of occultations. These are found in astronomy magazines and some of the 'quality' newspapers. Finding two planets within the field of view of a normal focal length lens is quite a common occurrence: three is by no means unusual, but thereafter the event becomes rarer. (Five planets – Mercury, Venus, Mars, Jupiter and Saturn – were relatively close together in the constellation Capricornus in February 1962 but they were too close to the Sun to be viewed from Earth.)

CHAPTER TEN

Comets, Zodiacal Light and Aurorae

Halley's Comet in 1985–6 was without doubt a great disappointment for members of the general public in the northern hemisphere. Although astronomers had warned that it would not be a bright object, such is the fame of this once-in-a-lifetime visitor that for many (even if they did manage to get a look at the small, diffuse ball in one of the telescopes made available to the public by astronomical societies) it was an anticlimax. Most of the comets which are discovered or return to the inner solar system each year are detected by inveterate, mostly amateur, comet hunters using binoculars – or by researchers studying photographic plates. The usually very dim comets receive considerable attention from cometary scientists – and virtually none from the man in the street. But, while not as frequent as in the last century, new comets occasionally appear that become bright, 'naked-eye' objects of great beauty and impact – and which are well within the grasp of the amateur's fixed camera. Comet Ikeya-Seki (most comets are named after their discoverers) in 1965, Bennett in 1970 and West in 1976 were examples.

Comets have been popularly associated throughout history with death, destruction, plague and other horrors. The folklore is interesting and entertaining, but comets have a much more serious place in astronomy. They are usually regarded as being the most primitive bodies within the solar system, having undergone relatively little change since it came into being about 4500 million years ago. Therefore, although comets vary greatly in their characteristics, the more that can be learned about them the greater the insight that can be gained into the evolution of the solar system. This is why comets have

received so much attention since the beginning of the space era and why Halley's Comet in particular was studied by a flotilla of probes from various countries.

When a comet is in deep space it essentially comprises a small nucleus just a few kilometres in size. Current theory (largely confirmed by the results from Halley) holds the nucleus to be a 'dirty snowball' – a mixture of frozen gases, particles of dust and other elements. As the comet nears the Sun, a coma (Latin for 'hair') develops. This is a tenuous halo which spreads out from the nucleus to a great distance in space and is composed of a mixture of dust and gases released through the sublimation of ice by the action of the Sun. Later still a tail of two components develops – a dust tail and an ion tail, the latter consisting of molecules released by the nucleus, that have been ionized by solar utraviolet and X-radiation. Electrically charged particles from the Sun (the solar wind) and pressure from solar radiation cause both tails to form in an anti-solar direction from the nucleus. Hence the tails follow the head of the comet as it approaches the Sun but – perhaps paradoxically at first sight – precede it on the journey away from it. It is, of course, the tails of comets which can be so spectacular and cover such a large area of

An excellent example of the pleasing compositions that a 'seeing eye' can produce using a fixed camera. Beyond the trees is Comet West photographed in March 1976 by Akira Fujii. He used a Nikon camera and a 35mm wide-angle lens at f/2. The exposure was twenty seconds on Kodak Tri-X film, which was developed in Fuji Pandol at 20°C (68°F) for ten minutes.

the sky – thereby presenting a marvellous subject for the photographer.

How bright and extensive a comet appears to observers on Earth depends upon a large number of factors, not all of which are understood. One which is readily apparent, however, concerns the relative positions of the comet and the Earth as the comet rounds the Sun. The reason why the 1985–6 visit of Halley's Comet was not one of the best arose from the fact that for some time around perihelion (the comet's closest point to the Sun), when the greatest activity develops, it was on the other side of the Sun when viewed from Earth and therefore was lost in the Sun's glare. The distance between comet and Earth on the incoming and outgoing passages is also important.

So a comet's brightness will vary from the extremely dim – such that it can be seen in telescopes only – to the very bright, when it may well be seen in daylight. The last occasion on which the latter occurred was early in 1910 when the Great Daylight Comet upstaged Halley's Comet which followed some weeks later. In the face of such differences it is difficult to give valid guidance to the newcomer to astrophotography, but one generalization may be proffered: if a comet is a naked-eye object then an attempt to photograph it with a fixed camera on a tripod is well worth while.

There is one feature of comets that works in the photographer's favour and which is frequently the cause of some confusion. Although it will be moving at high speed in absolute terms – Halley's speed at perihelion was around 200,000km/h (124,300mph) – when viewed from Earth it will not be speeding across the sky like a 'shooting star': it will move gradually against the backdrop of stars and a few hours will need to elapse for the movement to become clearly discernible. Over the course of several nights, of course, this movement will become easily apparent.

Comets are extended objects so, as with everyday objects, the measure of the speed of a lens is focal ratio. Because they typically brighten around perihelion, when they are at their best they are often located in the western or eastern skies during evening twilight or dawn. The sky will therefore be relatively light, so that lengthy exposures are not possible. There is an advantage in these conditions which was mentioned in the last chapter – the eye may see little colour, but film often records delightful hues which result in a most attractive pictorial image. If the comet is still up some time after the Sun has set, light pollution may become a problem near towns.

Should a naked-eye comet appear it is almost certain that it will be well covered in the media, with newspapers giving details of the time and place in the sky that it will be visible, weather permitting. Estimates of the length of the tails may well be given in advance and from that the most likely suitable focal length can be worked out as in Chapter 8. Alternatively, direct observation can eventually establish the most suitable focal length. If the tail structure develops well it is probable that a 50mm focal length lens will be required. With the prospect of a light, colourful sky – as opposed to the darkness of a night image – quality is important, and it is recommended that a compromise on film speed should be adopted with the use of an ISO400 film.

With the lens at its fastest focal ratio, and observing the basic photographic drill (sturdy tripod, black card and so on), a series of exposures from around five seconds, up to perhaps one minute in five-second increments, should be given. Some star trailing will take place in the longer exposures, but this is perfectly acceptable since it is the comet that is the prime target. Assuming that the weather is good and that the comet is visible on a number of days or nights, modifications to the bracketing programme can be introduced if the first results are not satisfactory. If the comet becomes very bright and the first results suggest the possibility, it would be worth while trying a slower film of ISO200 in the interests of better quality.

Should the comet be a bright object at dusk or dawn, this again would be an occasion when the value of an aperture-priority automatic exposure system – with careful notes being made of the shutter speeds selected by the camera – and the results obtained on colour negative film could be explored. The image size of the comet (according to focal length selected) will affect the metering mode chosen if more than one mode is available.

Again assuming a very bright comet, a keen black and white photographer might wish to experiment with photographing the ion and dust tails. Since the dust tail is yellowish in colour (due to back scatter of sunlight towards the observer) and emission from the ion tail is at the blue end of the spectrum, the use of a yellow or orange filter and a blue filter respectively could enhance the detail of the two features. Kodak Wratten filters type 21 and 47A or 47 respectively would be suitable. Clearly, to stand any chance of success with the use of filters (which attenuate the light transmitted) on a camera which is fixed and not on an equatorial mount, the comet would have to be extremely bright. In that event, ISO400 black and white film rated perhaps at ISO800 would be suitable.

The procedures suggested here would not have worked well with Halley's Comet photographed from the northern hemisphere in 1985–6. The comet did not develop an extensive enough tail structure nor was it bright enough to capture with basic photographic equipment. There will be others, however, and we are owed a bright one. Then capturing your first comet on film will be a prize indeed.

Zodiacal Light

Comets can be bright but are all too frequently dim: a genuine dim light phenomenon which none the less makes an intriguing picture is the zodiacal light. Quite probably it has been seen by many people – particularly those fortunate enough to take cruises to the tropics and the Equator – who confused it with the twilight.

The name zodiacal light stems quite logically from the fact that it stretches along the imaginary belt in the sky that contains the paths of the Sun, Moon and planets. It may be seen after astronomical twilight ends during the evenings (i.e. when the Sun is more than eighteen degrees beneath the horizon) and for some time before the Sun reaches that position at dawn. The phenomenon is caused by dust in interplanetary space scattering sunlight, and is in fact regarded as the outer fringe of the solar corona. It appears as a luminous wedge or pyramid of light, approximately as bright as the Milky Way, with the widest and brightest area of the wedge on the horizon – that is, closest to the Sun.

A dark sky is essential (moonlight is again to be avoided) and zodiacal light is seen to best advantage within the tropics where (following the line of the ecliptic) it rises almost straight up from the horizon throughout the year. It is still clearly visible, however, in a dark sky outside the tropics where, in the northern hemisphere, it is best seen in the west after sunset in the spring and in the east before sunrise in the autumn. There the evening zodiacal light inclines to the left and in the early morning to the right (i.e. to the south in both cases), and under optimum conditions it can be seen stretching almost to the zenith. In the southern hemisphere outside the tropics these conditions are reversed; for example, the light is best seen in the west after sunset in autumn.

As with other astronomical objects, locating or recognizing the phenomenon may well be a little more difficult for newcomers than actually photographing it. Since the zodiacal light can last for an hour or so after twilight ends there is no rush. Given its extent, a 50mm or 35mm wide-angle lens is required and the camera needs to be loaded with ISO400 or 1000 film. Zodiacal light – like comets or nebulae – is an extended object and a fast focal ratio is therefore a critical factor. Using the slower of the suggested films, a sequence of time exposures, starting at two minutes and extending through four and eight minutes before ending on fifteen minutes, is suggested.

Although zodiacal light is essentially monochromatic, colour film results in a pleasing picture since star trails will be recorded. Greater accentuation of the phenomenon itself can be achieved by using an ISO400 black and white film, overdeveloping it by about 25 per cent and printing the resulting contrasty negative on a hard grade of paper.

A

As Orion sank towards the western horizon of Tenerife in April 1987 and a satellite moved through the sky above, they were accompanied by a prominent display of the Zodiacal light – a wedge of light along the ecliptic which is at a steep angle to the horizon during springtime evenings in the northern hemisphere. The original photograph (a) was shot on Agfachrome 1000RS Professional film during a ten minute time exposure: the lens used was a 35mm Nikkor at f/2.8. In September of the same year and the same location the Zodiacal light appeared before dawn in the eastern sky (b). The star trails at the top of the picture include Castor and Pollux in Gemini. Procyon in Canis Minor is the bright trail on the right and plainly seen in the upper centre of the Zodiacal light is the open star cluster Praesepe (or 'Beehive') in the constellation Cancer. The original image was also on Agfachrome 1000RS Professional film but the exposure was for fifteen minutes and the lens used a 24mm f/2.8 Nikkor.

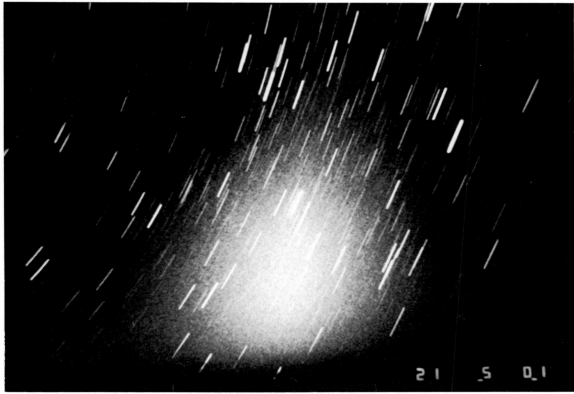

B

Aurorae

The *aurora borealis* (or northern lights) is something we all learned about at school. (The *aurora australis* is the southern-hemisphere equivalent but ground studies there have been hindered by the fact that the high southern latitudes contain few land areas.) Since the coming of the space age, research into the aurorae has intensified and few can have failed to be impressed by the images beamed back to control centres by spacecraft such as NASA's Dynamic Explorers showing a huge glowing oval, about 4500km (2800 miles) across, astride the geomagnetic pole and running through Siberia, Scandinavia, Greenland, Canada and Alaska. A new view of the aurora, indeed.

The complex interaction between solar activity, interplanetary plasma, the Earth's magnetic field and the atmosphere that results in the aurora is still being investigated, and questions remain unanswered. It is sufficient for our purposes to say that auroral activity occurs at about 90km (56 miles) and above in

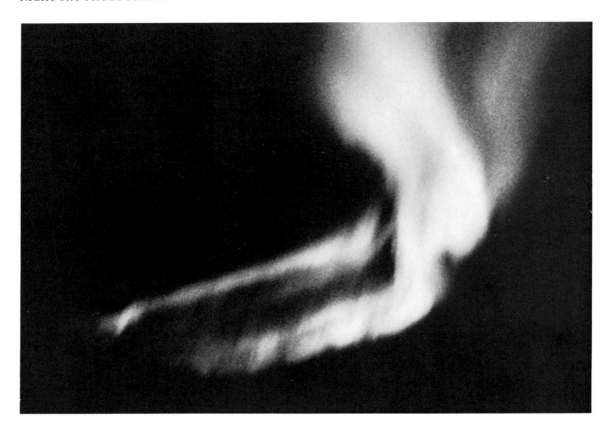

Colour film is inevitably the most popular choice for photographing many astronomical objects, and aurorae are no exception. But even in black and white the results can be very impressive. This print was made from an ISO1000 colour transparency exposed for five seconds using a 50mm f/1.4 Nikkor lens.

the upper atmosphere and tends to be linked to sunspot and solar flare activity. But even for those with scant technical interest, the spectacle of an aurora is well worth seeing and is a splendid subject for the astrophotograper.

On some occasions an aurora may be just a dim glow not unlike moonlight – but at other times we may be privileged to witness an exotic display of arcs, bands and rays in shades of green and red, which sometimes hang motionless in the sky and then suddenly start rapid shifts and undulations which seem as though they ought to be accompanied by suitable, awe-inspiring sounds – but which take place in utter silence.

Aurora brightness varies greatly from very dim to an intensity which can light up the surrounding countryside as though it were twilight. This variation in brightness and the large differences in speed of movement pose problems for the photographer, so that bracketing is once again essential. Using a fixed camera with a 50mm or wide-angle lens at maximum aperture (aurorae are extended objects), and loaded with ISO400 or 1000 colour film, exposures of up to one minute should be given for relatively dim and inactive aurorae. When they are bright and highly active a stepped series of exposures of about 2, 5 and 10 seconds should be given. Anything much in excess of this will risk overexposure and therefore desaturation of colour as well

as a merging of the features. Differences between the peak sensitivities of eye and film (and the different UV transmission characteristics of lenses) will not infrequently result in the colours of the photograph being different from the colours we see.

The opportunity to photograph aurorae varies according to geographical location. They occur essentially in high latitudes, although their activity moves farther south during periods of maximum sunspot activity. (The next solar maximum is scheduled to occur in 1990.) Figures published by the Aurora Section of the British Astronomical Association demonstrate the relative infrequency of observed aurorae in more southerly latitudes – and the increased frequency during a period of sunspot maximum (1979) compared with that of sunspot minimum (1986):

Geomagnetic Latitude (degrees*)	53	54	55	56	57	58	59	60	61	62
Visible aurorae: 1986	2	2	4	10	11	14	27	28	54	63
1979	8	9	20	23	25	62	90	104	138	140

(*Geomagnetic latitude differs slightly from normal geographic latitude.)

CHAPTER ELEVEN

Meteors, Satellites, Aircraft and 'UFOs'

Everybody at some time or other has seen a 'shooting star' – a brief trail of light in the night sky lasting for a fraction of a second. This effect is caused by a particle of interplanetary dust impacting the upper atmosphere of the Earth. The heat generated usually vaporizes the particle completely but a complex interaction results in the ionization of air molecules around and behind the particle – and this is the light trail that we see in the sky. The name meteor is given to this phenomenon; the actual particle of dust is called a meteoroid and any meteoroid which survives the passage through the Earth's atmosphere and reaches the surface is known as a meteorite.

Meteor trails occur in the lower levels of the thermosphere at an altitude of from 80 to 120km (50–74 miles). Entry speeds vary greatly, with an upper limit of around 70km/s (43 miles per second). Brightness levels, too, vary widely, with an effective lower limit (for the photographer) of magnitude 2, rising to the brightness of the planet Venus (magnitude −4) and beyond, when meteors are called fireballs and can be seen during the day.

Meteors can occur at any time of the night, but the hourly rate for what are called sporadic meteors (maybe five or so an hour) is low compared with periods of the year when the Earth encounters meteor streams. These streams are generally believed to originate from debris left by periodic comets as their orbit brings them into the inner solar system. When the Earth's orbit around the Sun takes it through or near the orbit of a comet a surge in the number of observed meteors takes place in what is called a meteor shower. The meteors then appear to radiate from the same point of the night sky at the same time each year. The particles are in fact moving on parallel paths and the appearance of radiating out from a point is an effect of perspective – in much the same way that when we stand on a bridge over a straight main road and look towards the horizon, the parallel lanes of the road appear to meet at the farthest point from us, although we know they do no such thing. None the less, the term 'radiant' is still used for the apparent point of origin of the meteors, and this is always identified by the name of the background constellation or principal star.

There are as many as 1500 active radiants, but the major meteor showers during the course of a year are:

Shower	Date	Maximum	Estimated number per hour at maximum
Quadrantids*	1–5 January	3–4 January	Up to 100
Eta Aquarids	1–12 May	5 May	20
Delta Aquarids	15 July–15 Aug.	28 July	35
Perseids	1–18 Aug.	12 Aug.	65
Orionids	17–26 Oct.	20 Oct.	35
Leonids†	14–20 Nov.	17 Nov.	Enormous variation with periodicity of 33 years
Geminids	4–16 Dec.	13–14 Dec.	50

*Named after the now defunct constellation Quadrans Muralis: the radiant is in the constellation Bootes.

†A meteor storm occurred in 1966 when the hourly rate in Arizona was over 150,000. It is due again in 1998–9.

How well a particular shower will perform in any one year cannot be predicted, but the time of the likely maximum hourly rate (given in the table) can be determined quite accurately. Even the more elusive sporadic meteors have a diurnal peak which occurs in the hours before dawn. This results from the fact that, as the Earth moves in its orbit around the Sun, an observer in the early hours of the morning is on the leading side and will see any meteors that are encountered entering the atmosphere head-on, with higher energies generated and therefore brighter trails. In the evening hours, this observer is on the trailing side of Earth with the meteors having to catch up and, even if successful, not entering the

This time exposure by Akira Fujii captured two Perseid meteors giving a classic demonstration of how meteors radiate from the area of the sky after which they are named—in this case the constellation of Perseus. The smaller of the two trails is in fact still within the bounds of Perseus. At the bottom left can be seen the Pleiades, and towards the top right is the M31 Great Galaxy in Andromeda. The original picture was exposed on Fujichrome 400 film in a Canon F1 camera with a f/1.4 24mm wide-angle lens fitted.

atmosphere at such high speed. An analogy is that of a motor vehicle travelling at 100km/h (62mph) hitting one travelling at 95km/h (59mph) head-on (the cumulative speed is 195km/h/121mph), and of the same vehicle closing up behind the other and hitting it at only 5km/h (3mph). The diagram explains the point.

So, we have a general indication of the times of the year and the nights when there is the best chance of observing meteors, although skill and luck are obviously important. The task facing the astrophotographer is intriguing. We are dealing once again with point sources, but there is a major difference compared with photography of the stars. When the stars are photographed with a fixed camera (of course, the effect is even more marked with a driven camera) their apparent movement is very slight and, in effect, for the duration of the exposure the light falls on the same area of film. (We are not concerned here with deliberately trying to record star trails.) However, meteor trails move across the film – and in a period of time ranging from $\frac{1}{10}$ to $\frac{8}{10}$ of a second. It may sound quite encouraging to talk about meteor trails of, for example, magnitude 1, but this is far from being the same as a star of magnitude 1 that is steadily building up an image on film over twenty seconds or more.

As we have seen, the diameter of the lens is the most crucial factor in the photography of point sources, so one's natural inclination might be to opt for the long, large-diameter lenses discussed in earlier chapters. The drawback is their relatively small fields of view, which make the chances of capturing meteors all the slimmer. If we go to the opposite extreme, a wide-angle lens gives a far greater chance of including a meteor in its field of view, but because it has a relatively small diameter the meteor might appear very faint or not be recorded at all on the film. Compromise is the best solution – in the shape of the well-established 'normal' 50mm focal length lens, particularly if it is f/1.8 or even faster. This gives the very reasonable 27 × 40 degree field of view and a diameter of 28mm (or more with faster lenses).

As in star photography, high film speeds may appear attractive but must be selected with careful consideration of the quality of the sky in your area. Remember that, used wide open, the lens diameter will be doing its best with point sources but that at the same time the fast focal ratio will cause the film to record any light pollution rapidly. If the sky is dark and of good quality there is every reason to select one of the high-speed films in the ISO 1000 range: with meteors there are no worries about reciprocity failure over lengthy exposures and films capable of maximizing the very brief light-burst are at a premium. Most meteor photography specialists use

This diagram explains why meteors are usually better seen in the small hours of the morning, rather than earlier in the night. Because of the movement of the Earth in its orbit, an observer on the leading side of the Earth as the end of night approaches sees meteors hitting the atmosphere head on and at much higher speeds than during the evening, when the meteors are having to catch up with the Earth.

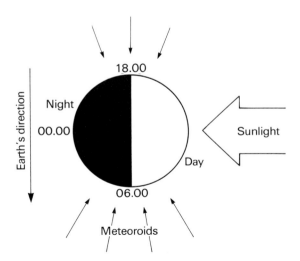

black and white film but there is no reason at all why colour film should not be used if the newcomer wishes it – in fact, there is greater choice among very high-speed colour films even if the price is higher.

Although it may seem surprising, it is not advisable to centre the radiant in the camera's field of view. If any meteors are captured they will be seen head-on as points of light rather than as trails. Based on observations over some years, meteor specialists advise pointing the camera at an elevation of 50 degrees to the horizon and from 30 to 45 degrees on either side of the radiant. Using an elevation of 30 degrees is likely to produce a higher yield of fireballs.

The general advice on procedures given in Chapter 5 applies, and since meteor photography tends by definition to be a somewhat protracted business if tackled at all seriously, you should have some means to hand of dealing with the formation of dew on lenses. Meteor photography comes into the category of patrol photography – it is obviously impossible to react fast enough to photograph meteors as they occur, and a series of time exposures must therefore be made of a duration and over a period that you decide upon. It is difficult to give general advice on this but in essence the length of separate exposures must depend on the darkness of the sky. If the sky is good, exposures of up to ten minutes or so should be possible with little risk of sky fog – particularly if a medium-fast ISO400 film is being used. The drawback of lengthy exposures with a fixed camera is that extensive star trails tend to hide any meteor trails, particularly if they are faint and running with the trails.

If the sky is average or poor then the best tactic is to hold exposures down to no more than a minute or so; this is heavy on film but may be necessary in terms of the potential results. If you have not carried this out before, a sensible thing to do before a meteor shower is expected is to make some test exposures lasting for say 1, 5, 10 and 15 minutes on the type of film to be used and from the site proposed. This will establish the quality of the sky and the tactics that must be pursued. The light pollution in my home area is bad, and at f/2.8 using an ISO400 film the maximum time exposure possible during a patrol is no more than two minutes. In all cases, if a meteor is observed anywhere near the camera's field of view the exposure should be ended immediately; if it is continued at all the precious trail image might be lost in background fog.

In its past, the Earth – like most other bodies in the solar system – has been subjected to meteoritic bombardment of great intensity. There are relatively few cases of large bodies impacting the surface in recorded history, but this has not prevented the evolution of theories about the role of 'catastrophism' in the Earth's history – for example, in the extinction of the dinosaurs. Meteors are at the opposite end of the size scale, but occasionally we are reminded of what might be. On 10 August 1972, for example, a fireball was seen over a large area of the USA and Canada in broad daylight. Fortunately, the oblique angle of its approach and its high velocity caused it to skip out of the atmosphere. Its weight was estimated to be a possible 1000 tons and, if it had impacted, the energies released would have been equivalent to a thermonuclear explosion. It did not – and, more prosaically, one lesson of its appearance was the need to carry a camera at all times. Pictures taken of the fireball as it passed over the Teton Mountains were splendid.

Satellites

Man-made satellites in orbit about the Earth are much more predictable than meteors, although natural forces acting on them may cause them to appear a little later or earlier than predicted. Military radars currently track some 6000 objects in space – many of which are defunct spacecraft and the remnants of numerous launch vehicles which well qualify for the description of space junk – and at any one time perhaps 500 of these are above the horizon.

Earth-orbiting satellites shine by reflected sunlight, so it follows that they are typically seen some time after sunset and before sunrise against the darkness of the sky above. Depending on how far the Sun is beneath the horizon and the altitude of the satellite, it will either remain lit by sunlight for its entire passage overhead or enter the eclipse caused by the Earth's shadow (in the evening) or come out of it (in the early morning) part way through its passage above the observer's head. Not infrequently the surface of a satellite catches sunlight at a critical angle and a brief flash is seen – doubtless the cause of some UFO reports.

Those satellites seen by the naked eye or binoculars are in two broad categories. Weather and earth resources satellites (as well as many military spacecraft) are in what are usually called polar orbits, in which they travel in a north–south/south–north direction and cross the Equator more or less at right angles. This orbit is selected because over a given period all of the Earth's surface passes beneath the satellite's cameras or other sensors. Many other satellites are in orbits which do not take them so far to the north and south of the Equator – thus one which is said to be in a 50-degree inclination orbit will never pass beyond 50 degrees north or south latitude.

Depending upon their purpose, satellites differ too in their altitude (and therefore the time it takes them to complete an orbit) and the speed with which they move across the sky. The lower they are the faster they must travel. Thus a satellite at an altitude of about 200km (124 miles) will take around ninety minutes to complete an orbit of the Earth, and will move across the sky in one observer's field of view in perhaps two minutes. Another at an altitude of 5000km (3000 miles) or more could easily take three hours to circle the Earth and from ten to fifteen minutes at least to pass across the sky as seen from one vantage point.

Brightness also varies enormously depending on such features as the size and shape of the vehicle, as well as its altitude and the phase angle of the Sun. Many satellites require binoculars to be seen; others such as the Soviet space stations Salyut and Mir and the US space shuttle can be at least as bright as Sirius, the brightest star in the sky, and are easily seen with the naked eye. Similarly, whereas satellites usually move in their orbits with apparent ease and grace, there can be occasions of great drama – as when a spacecraft re-enters the Earth's lower atmosphere in a brilliant firework display or (as has happened in recent years) a Soviet Soyuz manned spacecraft approaches and docks with Salyut or Mir. Not infrequently, redundant parts of rockets once used to launch spacecraft can be seen tumbling end over end and periodically flashing as they orbit overhead.

During any period of observing it is very likely that a satellite of some kind will be seen. This is of little use, however, for those wishing to make a study of them whether with a camera or the eye, but it is worth enquiring of astronomical associations for details of the passage of satellites. According to taste you can either draw the track of a satellite across a geographical map and estimate its path relative to the viewing site, or (with appropriate information on its position in right ascension and declination at given times) across a star chart. Once information about the track and time is available, photography is quite straightforward.

Fortunately, satellites are point sources which are sometimes brighter, and invariably moving much more slowly, than meteors. Moreover, the advance information about their orbits means that, although there may

At the start of its second orbit after launch from the Kennedy Space Center, the space shuttle orbiter Columbia can be seen flying over southern England during the early evening of 28 November 1983. The vehicle was carrying the European Space Agency's Spacelab module on its first flight. This exposure was for forty-five seconds on Tri-X film and an f/2.8 24mm Nikkor wide-angle lens was used. Columbia was already in the field of view to the west when the exposure was begun, and it moved into eclipse almost at zenith. Vega in Lyra is the bright star towards the top left and the handle of the 'Dipper' (Ursa Major) can be seen over the poplar at the bottom right. The light on the horizon is a mixture of twilight and pollution.

be some small discrepancies, you can await their appearance without the need to adopt the patrol approach necessary with meteors. Once again the standard 50mm lens at maximum aperture provides both reasonable speed and large sky coverage which will be welcome to the novice. (Later, when experience has been gained and the passage of a satellite can be predicted with greater accuracy, longer focal length and faster lenses can be used.) Because the shutter is rarely held open for more than around thirty seconds, there is little fear of light pollution having too much effect on the image – particularly as there is no need to use a very high speed film: ISO400 (colour or black and white) is entirely satisfactory.

The normal basic procedures described in Chapter 5 may be applied to photographing satellites, but once the camera has been aimed at the target area of the sky it helps to memorize quite accurately the area of the sky covered by the lens's field of view, or even to draw a rough sketch map. When the satellite has been spotted, open the shutter on the 'B' setting using the black card, wait until the satellite is just a short way from the edge of the field of view, withdraw the card and then cover the lens again once the satellite has moved out of the target area. Of course, there is no reason at all why an exposure should not be begun or ended with a satellite in the middle of the field of view, but for obvious reasons this is more likely to occur when the satellite has been spotted at the last moment or has moved unseen and unexpected into an exposure being made for other reasons.

Your notes should include not only details of the lens and exposure but timings for the entry and (if possible) exit of a satellite from the camera's field of view, together with information about the location's longitude and latitude and the star fields included in the image. If there is then any subsequent query about the identity of the satellite the image with the supporting details should provide the answer.

If a satellite's passage is across the entire sky as seen from the photography site and is picked up very early, there is a temptation to try a series of pictures. Using a single camera this should only be attempted after having practised smooth and efficient readjustment of the tripod/camera pointing angle between exposures. It is far better to get one excellent image of a satellite (as near to zenith as possible) than risk knocking the tripod over, or having some similar mishap. If maximum coverage is required, it is sensible to arrange two cameras on two tripods pointing to different parts of the sky.

Aircraft – and UFOs

Many images of meteors and satellites are quite unmistakeable. Meteors range from faint and delicate, needle-like traces to the far more robust and dense trail of a fireball. Satellite trails are often of uniform density, although where they enter or leave eclipse there may well be a 'feathering' effect before the reflections from the spacecraft are extinguished. Sometimes, however, the trail may be broken into segments as a satellite rotates or tumbles, while somewhat less dramatic perturbations of this kind may introduce a pulsing of the trail which is seen under a glass only. Under less than perfect sky conditions (and if visual observations were not made at the same time) it can be difficult to decide on the likely cause of some trails – and this situation is compounded by aircraft lights.

Civilian airliners display a battery of lights. A constant red light is located at the end of the port wing and a constant green light on the starboard. A constant white light is usually fixed to the vertical stabilizer, and located both above and below the fuselage are flashing anti-collision beacons (usually orange in colour). Finally, very bright landing lights on the leading edges of the inner wings are typically switched on at night as a collision-avoidance measure once an aircraft has

These two images were taken during an automated camera patrol. The aircraft on the right passed directly above the camera and its full complement of strobe and fixed lights was recorded. The aircraft on the left was probably banking, so fewer lights were recorded of which one at least was a flashing strobe. At critical angles and without visible strobes aircraft can resemble satellites in the trail they leave on film—and on those relatively rare occasions careful analysis is required to identify them accurately.

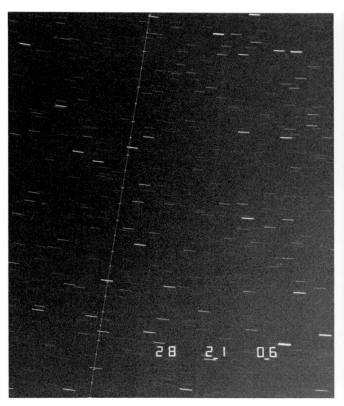

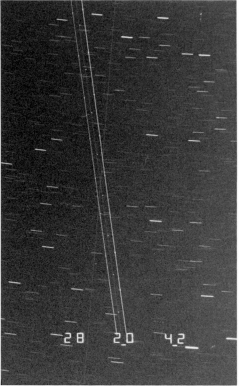

IFO (identified flying object): these two images are of the Corvus and Crater/Hydra region of the sky centred at −20° declination and were obtained during a programme of fixed-camera constellation photography. (North is at the top.) Two twenty-second time exposures were made (the first at the top) using an f/1.4 35mm Nikkor and Agfachrome 1000RS Professional film. During the photography no movement in the sky was observed but when the film was processed two short trails were revealed quite clearly. This indicated a bright object, but one at a considerable altitude and therefore moving quite slowly in a southerly direction. The object was subsequently identified by Russell Eberst as the largest remnant of the Pageos balloon satellite that was launched in 1966 and which disintegrated in 1975. It takes about 180 minutes to orbit the Earth in a near polar orbit.

descended below 3000m (10,000 feet).

When seen (or photographed) from directly below at night, an aircraft cannot be mistaken for anything else. As angles get more oblique, however, an image can become less easy to interpret and the presence of light cirrus cloud can complicate the problem. The illustrations on the previous page were taken during an automated camera patrol: the one on the right shows an aircraft trail from beneath, and the one on the left when the aircraft was at an angle to the camera. Both interpreta-

tions are indisputable, but it only needs the flashing strobe lights to be hidden from the camera for a teaser to be set for the newcomer to astrophotography – and sometimes for the more experienced! Often other evidence (knowledge of satellite passes or aircraft movements) will provide the answer, but this is not always the case.

This leads to the occasional need for detective work to resolve a mystery. I live about 60km (37 miles) south-west of an airport, and under one of the main approach paths. After taking up astrophotography some years ago I was puzzled initially by seemingly stationary bright lights to the south-west of the camera site. Thorough observation over a short period revealed these to be landing lights on aircraft in a 'head-on' approach a considerable distance away. No engine noise was audible, lateral movement was minimal and over a period of a few minutes there was no apparent movement of the light source. If observation was sustained long enough the eventual movement of the aircraft was clearly revealed – but this type of sighting may well be the origin of some UFO incidents.

Sometimes, even for the knowledgeable, celestial objects can provide a brief puzzle. During one evening's photography in the spring I saw a bright point of light in which green and red elements were discernible to the north-east – in the general direction of the airport. My instant reaction was to assume that an aircraft had just taken off (and to beware of letting it intrude into a picture). A few minutes later I noticed that the light was still in the same position – and thought that a helicopter might be operating in that area. After a further few minutes, with the light still approximately in the same position, the obvious truth dawned: the beautiful star Vega was rising and displaying some of the classic features of twinkling (or scintillation) when atmospheric turbulence refracts the light from a star and can often cause flashes of different colours.

I have never seen or photographed an object that later research and analysis failed to identify convincingly. Those faced with an object in the sky which puzzles them should endeavour to make full notes of the place, time, direction, elevation and any other relevant details. If at all possible it should be photographed with a series of time exposures (say 5, 10, 20 and 30 seconds on ISO400 film or faster) that should record background stars if the sky is clear. If time allows, use lenses of different focal lengths. In at least some of the pictures a foreground – even if a totally dark hedge, trees or house – should be included. The notes should contain the precise time at which each exposure was begun. It will be surprising if any mystery remains after subsequent analysis of notes and pictures.

CHAPTER TWELVE

The Way Ahead

Having reached this point after sampling previous chapters, some readers may have decided that observing rather than photography holds the main attraction for them. Others may have worked through the book in a determined way, taking photographs and steadily gaining knowledge about the sky and the photographic skills used in recording its greatly varied treasures. With luck the hard work will have been rewarded and photographs will have been produced that, compared with those in the astronomy magazines, can be said at the very least to be showing promise. The sole purpose of this book has been to bring readers to this stage where the obvious question is where to go from here. This chapter outlines the route ahead.

Camera Drives

As we turn to photographing more difficult celestial objects which require many minutes of exposure, the performance of even the fastest films used in a fixed camera is outpaced and we must look to equipment which enables us to track the stars – a reference to which appeared in Chapter 8 with the proposed use of the Haig manual guider as a first experiment.

Many astronomical objects cover large areas of the sky, and while we are no longer discussing the use of fixed or undriven cameras, those with ordinary photographic lenses fitted still have an important role to play. The means of enabling them to track the stars lies in two directions – dedicated camera drives and telescopes upon which they will ride 'piggy back'.

Various dedicated drives are available commercially. Some are quite simple: powered by clockwork or by a battery-driven

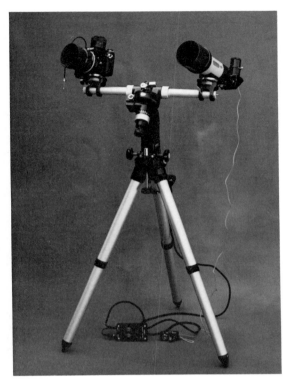

(*Above left*) **A modestly priced, battery-powered camera platform mounted on a tripod. This Astro Systems unit has a facility for polar alignment and is shown with a cross axis capable of carrying two cameras, or one camera and a guidescope. Since neither a second camera nor a guidescope is fitted here, the single camera needs to be balanced by weights. A unit of this type is satisfactory for time exposures that last some minutes using wide-angle or normal (50mm) focal length lenses.**

(*Above right*) **A more advanced battery-powered camera platform/guider with guidescope fitted. On the ground, on the left, is the battery pack and hand control unit which is used to modify the speed of the motor when guiding. The smaller unit to the right is a battery pack and dimmer switch which supplies light to the cross hairs of the illuminated reticle eyepiece fitted to the guidescope.**

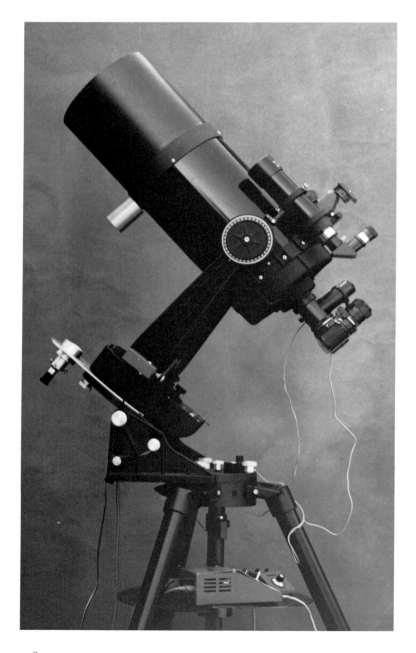

A 20cm aperture, 2000mm focal length Schmidt-Cassegrain telescope prepared for deep-sky photography using off-axis guiding via a unit fitted between the camera and the rear cell of the telescope. Noticeable features are the large dew cap with counterweights beneath it, the permanent piggy-back camera mount (not in use) at the top rear beside the guidescope, and the polar axis finder projecting to the left.

motor, they perform well and at least one currently available, modestly priced model has a motor which can be switched to operate in the southern hemisphere. Often, other attachments can be added – for example one to control the speed of the motor and thus make corrections in right ascension so that correct tracking is maintained. An important point to be made here is that, no matter what any advertising may say, even when a camera mount or telescope is correctly aligned on the celestial pole and the equipment is performing to specification, the gears and other mechanical components of the system cannot of themselves track a chosen celestial object with absolute accuracy. This is of no great significance when wide-angle and lenses of normal focal length are in use, but once a focal length of around 100mm is reached a control unit is required which allows the photographer – while monitoring the target's position – to make small adjustments to the speed of the motor. This is known as 'guiding'.

The mounts usually have a boom that is driven by the motor. Cameras can be placed at both ends, but more usually one end is used for a guidescope. This is focused on the target object which the photographer tracks throughout the exposure, making adjustments as necessary with a hand control. The units are portable, and are particularly well suited for low-power photography when travelling is involved. The more expensive models make better provision for accurate alignment on the celestial pole and are comparable in essentials to the capability of small telescopes. Simple, lower-priced mounts are suitable for taking good-quality constellation images over a course of minutes with cameras fitted with wide-angle lenses and lenses of

normal focal length. More expensive units can perform well up to 200 or 300mm focal lengths but in my experience that should be regarded as the limit. By that time we are approaching the territory of the telescope.

Telescopes

We have finally reached the instrument that for most people is the very essence of astronomy and which (for the very good reasons stated at the beginning of the book) we have been ignoring. Even now I am not going into detail about the innumerable types that are available: there are many books of advice and much guidance in the astronomy magazines. Here, quite arbitrarily, I shall talk about photographic applications using one of the most popular types of commercially produced telescopes – a 20cm aperture f/10 model with a focal length of 2000mm. Its optical system embraces both lenses and mirrors (not unlike the mirror-reflex photo lenses discussed previously) and is called a Schmidt-Cassegrain, in honour of two pioneers whose optical researches (greatly separated in time) made a contribution to this eventual result.

This excellent and highly versatile telescope (which has the generic name of reflector to differentiate it from a telescope using lenses only which is called a refractor) can be fully equipped not only with numerous eyepieces of various powers but with a dual-axis drive corrector for the astrophotographer to make corrections in both declination and right ascension. Although it may seem surprising, it makes an admirable mount on which to 'piggy back' the camera, fitted with its own lenses. There are many popular astronomical objects – such as the famous M31 spiral

The major observatories and telescopes are
frequently dramatic subjects for photographs and,
while not strictly a part of astrophotography as
such, the amateur should seize any opportunity to
visit and photograph the installations, for such
visits both further our knowledge and inspire.
Picture (a) is an aerial view of the great 305m
diameter radio telescope dish set in a natural
limestone hollow in the jungle clad mountains
south of Arecibo in Puerto Rico. The telescope
relies on the Earth's rotation to bring celestial
objects into view. Another of the world's great
radio telescopes (b) is the Very Large Array (VLA)
on the plains of San Augustin near Socorro in New
Mexico, USA *(overleaf)*. Twenty-seven individual
antennae, each 25m in diameter, are arranged
along three equally spaced radial arms, forming a
Y-shaped array. Two of the arms are 21km long
and one just over 19km. When furthest away from
one another on the arms the antennae yield the
highest resolution astronomical data – but they are
at their most dramatic photographically when
close together as here. Both pictures were taken
with a Hasselblad camera, fitted with a 150mm f/4
and 80mm f/2.8 lens respectively, and loaded with
Tri-X film.

A

B

galaxy in Andromeda – which are too large to fit within the 35mm film frame when photographed through a 2000mm focal length instrument. So the solution is to purchase, or make, a special fitting which attaches permanently to the top of the telescope at the back and to which the camera can be clamped. The camera is then fitted with a more convenient 300 or 400mm focal length lens to record the glories of M31 and is aligned along the top of the telescope barrel – the camera's normal viewfinder being used to frame the galaxy.

The telescope, of course, plays a vital role. Having been polar aligned correctly, it will be tracking in right ascension quite well. It may be that the focal length of the lenses being

used shows few signs of the minor imperfections in the rate at which the telescope is being driven by its motor, but most photographers will none the less usually guide it manually. A star diagonal is fitted at the rear cell of the telescope (this directs the light rays upwards at right angles) and in it is placed an illuminated reticle. This is a high-power eyepiece with single or double cross-hairs that are illuminated by a red light of controllable brightness. The telescope is aimed at the area to be photographed, and when the correct field of view for the camera lens has been confirmed, a target star is focused in the telescope's eyepiece. Then, throughout the exposure, a hand control unit is used to make slight adjustments in right ascension (and, less likely, in declination) so that the target star remains on the illuminated cross-hair.

This is an admirable way of guiding for moderate focal length photography because, obviously, if a 2000mm telescope is being used for the guiding and is holding steady on a target star, the results produced by a lens of only 300 or 400mm focal length should be extremely satisfactory.

But, of course, the telescope does exist for photography in its own right. The camera lens is now detached and, by means of an adapter and a T-ring suited to the individual camera, the camera is fitted to the rear end of the telescope. Now the skies are viewed through f/10 optics of 2000mm focal length. This is called prime focus photography. The focal length is such that the Moon and Sun fit conveniently into the 35mm film frame. When other objects are too large a tele-compressor lens can be fitted which reduces the telescope to an effective f/5 1000mm system, which is faster, of course.

Since the photography is taking place through the main lens of the telescope the problem arises of guiding during lengthy time exposures of deep-sky objects. This is usually solved by a technique known as off-axis guiding. A hollow 'T'-shaped accessory screws directly into the rear cell of the telescope and the camera is fitted to the other end to receive the light down the tube. Part of the way down the guider tube is a small prism which reflects light from the edge of the field of view and directs it up at right angles to the illuminated reticle, which is fitted at the top of the long stem of the 'T' accessory. A suitable star is selected as the target for the illuminated cross-hairs and, once the exposure has been begun,

any drift is revealed by the star's beginning to move off the hairs. This movement is corrected (as with the piggy-back photography) by manipulating the drive-corrector control unit. The technique sounds very straight-forward but is in fact demanding.

One more stage remains with the telescope so far as mainstream photography is concerned. A focal length of 2000mm is insufficient for some subjects — for photographing the Sun and Moon 'close up', or the planets, for example. At this stage the eyepieces, or oculars, used for visual observing are pressed into use. An eyepiece is screwed into the visual back of the telescope. A tele-extender, which is a projection tube, screws over the eyepiece and the camera fits at the other end of the tube — a technique known as eyepiece projection photography. The eyepiece controls the degree of magnification obtained and photography of planets is frequently conducted at the astonishing focal lengths (to the ordinary photographer) of over 28,000mm at f/140.

Films and Filters

Such a low-value focal ratio inevitably raises the issue of film — particularly as the spectre of reciprocity failure affecting exposures of many minutes has risen on a number of occasions in previous chapters. Deep-sky photography is the realm of the serious astrophotographer and the professional observatories. Over the years Eastman Kodak has evolved a number of products for the observatories that were designed with specific sensitivities and to reduce reciprocity failure to a minimum. These films and plates are still used but the technique of hypersensitization has grown greatly in popularity in recent years and is used widely by advanced amateurs and in observatories.

In this technique, film is baked in a special container in a 'forming gas' mixture of nitrogen and hydrogen for several days at around 30°C (86°F). A small amount of fog occurs, but reciprocity failure is greatly reduced and certain films exhibit what can only be described as remarkable speed gains. Kodak Technical Pan 2415 is one of the most successful of the hypersensitized films and 10 × speed gains are claimed for it. The equipment for sensitizing films and treated films themselves are available from a major US supplier (see Sources and Information). For many years, dedicated astrophotographers reduced reciprocity failure by using specially constructed 'cold' cameras containing dry ice which chilled the emulsion. The technique was very demanding but introduced little fog into the emulsion and colour balance was scarcely affected. It seems fair to conclude, however, that hypersensitization of film has largely superseded this technique among deep-sky photographers.

Specialist filters have their part to play, of course. For some years broad-band filters have been available for both viewing and photographing the Sun. Perhaps the best known are glass-coated with Inconel – an alloy of iron, cobalt and nickel – which rejects 99.999 per cent of solar radiation. An aluminized mylar product is popular in the USA although if uncorrected this results in the appearance of a blue Sun. Study of more specific parts of the Sun can be conducted using specially constructed filters, which pass only a very small part of the spectrum – that concentrated at 6562.8Å (known as the hydrogen alpha line) – to reveal prominences, flares and other activity which are not visible through the broad-band filters. These filters are, however, expensive. Filters of another kind that are well worth examining are those designed to deal with the worst effects of light pollution – and which at the same time enhance contrast, to distinguish faint objects such as planetary and emission nebulae. Again they are not inexpensive but should be considered if bad skies are a severe problem.

It comes as no surprise that the computer and electronics industries have made themselves felt in astronomy. Telescopes that are computer controlled and can find a selection of astronomical objects from memory have been available commercially for several years. Computer and astronomy enthusiasts are now joining forces to produce systems which a few years ago would scarcely have been found in professional observatories. It seems possible, too, that guiding in astrophotography will be given over to electronics in the next few years. Even the ubiquitous charge-coupled device (CCD) is now being used by amateurs as an imaging medium. In this context (and that of announcements about solid-state cameras making the conventional camera obsolete) a few words are needed.

The problem of reciprocity failure has appeared quite frequently in these pages. One of the great advantages of the CCD is that its response to light is linear, i.e. in direct proportion to exposure time. In addition, it is extremely sensitive to light from faint objects, is able to handle great extremes of contrast, and its output can be readily prepared for digital analysis by the computer. Against that, some CCDs need to be kept at very low temperatures, and their expense, relatively poor resolution and extremely small size (a centimetre or two square compared with the size of a large photographic plate) are disadvantages. But in fact, the two systems are complementary: photography with its high resolution over a wide area is ideally suited for sky surveys and search programmes to locate bodies moving relative to the star background. The CCD is ideally suited for imaging efficiently bodies which have already been located or whose location is being predicted – as in the case of the recovery of Halley's Comet in 1982. Technical progress seems likely to be made in the years ahead in both professional and amateur astrophotography – and both silver-halide photography and electronic systems will have their part to play.

For anyone making progress with astrophotography it is worth thinking seriously about moving onwards into the new areas outlined in this chapter. Excellent work can be done with the fixed camera but, once you progress to a driven camera, the metaphorical chains are broken and you are free to go where your skill can take you.

Postscript

One of the fascinating things about astronomy is the contribution that amateurs can make to new knowledge. It would be understandable to assume that all areas of the sky are studied continuously by professional astronomers working in observatories around the world. In fact such astronomers number merely a few thousands: possibly half or more of them are theoreticians who rarely *look* at the sky or who are working in radio and other wavelengths. Many of the remainder will be fighting for very limited observing time in the pursuit of important but very restricted research projects. Hardly any will ever conduct broad, sweeping surveys of the night sky.

This is where amateur observers and astrophotographers have a role to play. For example, in the study of the Moon, planets, asteroids, meteors or variable stars – and in the search for comets and novae – it is amateurs who as a group can contribute the time, the enthusiasm and the developing skills that have come to be so highly regarded by professional astronomers. In the eyes of the general public, astronomy is regarded as a high-technology science which depends on sophisticated, costly telescopes and spacecraft. It is in fact a revelation to realize how much can be achieved with a pair of binoculars – or even the naked eye.

In the late 1960s and early 1970s, I was much involved with the photographic programmes being conducted during NASA's Apollo lunar missions. When looking, in particular, at the superb, high-resolution images of the Moon's surface obtained by mapping cameras flown from Apollo 15 and others thereafter, it was easy to question why anybody anywhere back on Earth should henceforth bother to try and photograph the Moon. Shortly afterwards, I took up astrophotography seriously and the answer was provided: nothing I could produce could rival the Apollo images, but equally there was nothing to compare with the thrill of roaming over the lunar maria and mountains with the eyepiece of a telescope and (whatever the problems with the Earth's atmosphere) recording these features personally on photographic film.

This is the delight of astronomy: our interest may be more casual than those who devote much time, effort and skill to 'patrol' activities or other programmes – but all can share in the emotions roused by the never-ending mystery, drama and beauty of the sky.

Astrophotographers have an advantage over their colleagues in virtually all other branches of photography, for in a very real sense we can begin to appreciate the true meaning of infinity. If this book helps readers part of the way towards that appreciation I will be well content.

May we all successfully defy Spode's Law – and enjoy clear, dark skies!

Sources and Information

Societies

The newcomer to astrophotography may wish to join a local astronomy society, but where this is not possible (or additionally) two national bodies in Britain, with various specialist sections, are:

British Astronomical Association, Burlington House, Piccadilly, London W1V 9AG.

Junior Astronomical Society, c/o the Enrolment Secretary, 22 Queensthorpe Road, London SE26 4PH. (Founded 'to aid the beginner in astronomy', irrespective of age.)

A specialist group is the British Meteor Society, 26 Adrian Street, Dover, Kent CT17 9AT.

Specialist Astronomical Retailers

Astro Systems Limited, 24 Old Bedford Road, Luton, Beds LU2 7NR (0582-421136)

Broadhurst, Clarkson & Fuller Limited, Telescope House, 63 Farringdon Road, London EC1M 3JB (01-405 2156)

Equipment for hypersensitizing films and treated films can be purchased from Lumicon, 2111 Research Drive, Livermore, California 94550, USA.

Magazines

Sky and Telescope and *Astronomy* are monthly US magazines which are sold worldwide. Both are available on direct subscription, and *Astronomy* from retail outlets in the UK. In addition, the former is available on subscription from the British Astronomical Association in London.

Astronomy Now is a new British magazine that is available on bookstalls. It is hoped that it will become fully established and fulfil a long-felt need.

Sky Calendar is a monthly, illustrated, double-sided news-sheet highlighting forthcoming events – conjunctions, occultations, etc. – which is sent to subscribers well in advance and is highly recommended. It is obtainable from Sky Calendar, Abrams Planetarium, Michigan State University, East Lansing, Michigan 48824, USA.

A range of planispheres for various latitudes is published by George Philip & Son Ltd, 27a Floral Street, London WC2E 9DP.

Bibliography

General/Introductory

MOORE, P., *Exploring the Night Sky with Binoculars* (Cambridge University Press, 1986)

MOORE, P., *Stargazing: Astronomy Without a Telescope* (Angus & Robertson, 1985). An excellent general guide to naked-eye astronomy.

MUIRDEN, J., *The Amateur Astronomer's Handbook* (Harper & Row, 1983)

PELTHIER, L., *Guide to the Stars: Exploring the Sky with Binoculars* (Cambridge University Press, 1986)

Specific Themes

GREENLER, R., *Rainbows, Halos and Glories* (Cambridge University Press, 1980)

KING-HELE, D., *Observing Earth Satellites* (Macmillan, 1983)

MEADOWS, J., *Space Garbage: Comets, Meteors and Other Solar System Debris* (George Philip, 1985)

MEINEL, A. and M., *Sunsets, Twilights and Evening Skies* (Cambridge University Press, 1983)

MOORE, P., and HUNT, G., *The Atlas of the Solar System* (Mitchell Beazley, 1983). An extremely useful and comprehensive reference work about the bodies of the solar system from the viewpoint of space exploration and comparative planetology rather than astronomy.

NOYES, R.W., *The Sun, Our Star* (Harvard University Press, 1982)

WHIPPLE, F.L., *The Mystery of Comets* (Cambridge University Press, 1985)

Astrophotography

COVINGTON, M., *Astrophotography for the Amateur* (Cambridge University Press, 1985)

GORDON, B., *Astrophotography* (Willmann-Bell, 1983). Although published in the US, this book is available in the UK from Broadhurst, Clarkson & Fuller. Mr Gordon has an excellent 'no-nonsense' approach to the subject which concentrates on essentials and is particularly strong on exposure considerations.

LILLER, W., and MAYER, B., *The Cambridge Astronomy Guide: A Practical Introduction to Astronomy* (Cambridge University Press, 1985). Despite its title the emphasis of this cooperation between a professional and an amateur astronomer is on photography.

LITTLE, R.T., *Astrophotography: A Step-by-Step Approach* (Macmillan, 1986)

MALIN, D., and MURDIN, P., *Colours of the Stars* (Cambridge University Press, 1984). Not a 'how to' book but an in-depth treatment of the title theme with many magnificent illustrations.

Photography

Unfortunately there are few books on photographic technique and processing at the right level to be of significant help to those with scant background in photography.

Book of the Darkroom (Paterson Products Limited, 1987). A lucid and helpful guide to both black and white and colour processing. There are many advantages in doing one's own processing.

BUSSELLE, M., *The Photographer's Question & Answer Book* (Collins, 1987). Although ranging wide and aimed predominantly at everyday photography, there is much good sense lucidly presented in this book.

NEBLETTE, C.B., *Photographic Lenses* (Fountain Press, 1973). More advanced but extremely useful.

Practical Processing in Black-and-White Photography (Eastman Kodak – Fountain Press, 1978). A brief pamphlet but solid and helpful.

Index